WEATHER
made clear

By CAPTAIN DAVID C. HOLMES, U.S.N.

 STERLING
PUBLISHING CO., INC.   NEW YORK

OTHER BOOKS OF INTEREST

Basic Biology
The Microscope—and How to Use It
Experimenting with the Microscope
Electronic Brains—How Computers Work

Treasures of the Earth
What's New in Science
Pioneers in Science
Color Television—and How It Works
Miracle Drugs and the New Age of Medicine

ACKNOWLEDGMENTS

The author and publisher wish to thank the following for the use of the photographs in this book: Air Ministry, England; Air Weather Service, United States Air Force; American Aviation Inc.; American Red Cross; British Railways; Brookhaven National Laboratory; General Electric Research Laboratory; Hanford Atomic Products Operation; Her Majesty's Stationery Office, England; Los Alamos Scientific Laboratory; Meteorological Office, Berks., England; Prof. Stanley L. Miller, University of California at San Diego; National Aeronautics and Space Administration, Washington, D.C.; National Bureau of Standards; George Outram & Co. Ltd., Glasgow; Radio Corporation of America; Santa Fe Railway; Standard Oil Co. of N.J.; United States Air Force; United States Army; United States Atomic Energy Commission; United States Coast Guard; United States Department of Commerce, Weather Bureau; Wide World Photos.

CONTENTS

Foreword

THE ATMOSPHERE IS SO VAST THAT THERE ARE TWO million tons of it for each person on earth. Yet 99%— or 5,000,000,000,000,000 tons—lies within 19 miles of the earth's surface, encasing the globe in a soft, protective envelope. There is no other atmosphere like it in all the billions of space miles that scientists have been able to explore with telescopes and rockets. The atmosphere shields us from the heat of the sun and the deadly perils of outer space. It acts as a huge air conditioner to regulate the temperature of our world. It is a great wheel of electricity, of chemicals, and of water.

The complexity of contemporary life hinders our understanding and appreciation of the miracle of atmosphere. We are concerned primarily with its unpleasant aspects. We reflect upon it darkly when we are confronted with a fuel bill or a frozen radiator. When the forecaster commits himself to a sunny day and it rains, we regard this as a human failure. In the modern world it is sometimes hard to realize that weather, like the movement of the stars, is not regulated by a man-made ordinance, and that its principles are even now imperfectly interpreted and only partially understood.

Tycho Brahe's observatory, called Uraniborg (the "Castle of the Heavens"), was the first real observatory in the world. Built in 1572 with the help of the Danish king, Frederick II, it had fabulously elaborate and expensive equipment. Brahe was so emotional about the science of the heavens that in defending his beliefs in a duel he lost his nose, a sacrifice which has hardly been matched by today's scientists.

Although we have lived within the atmosphere since the beginning, we still seek the answers to many questions. What is the relationship between the circulations of the Northern and Southern Hemispheres? How does the atmosphere transform the sun's energy through various stages before it is ultimately dissipated? What is the effect of the variations in the earth's surface on our climate? These and many other riddles must be solved before we can hope to control or even make long-range predictions of the weather outside our homes.

Surely weather satellites and the use of radar to observe storms will be followed by many more new tools which will help us understand the mysteries of the ever-changing ocean of air. Man is ingenious and possessed by a certain questing bent. No one can doubt that we are on the threshold of incredible discoveries in weather science which will have an exciting impact upon the shape of the future.

Dr. S. Fred Singer
*Director, National
Weather Satellite
Center*

A majestic cumulo-nimbus towers over the land bringing thunder, lightning and rain.

1. The Last Unexplored Ocean

OVER OUR EARTH LIES A VAST, UNCHARTED, SHORE-less sea.

It undulates softly over the green and brown land bringing to us rain from the oceans, heat from the deserts, and cold from the arctic snow. Often this sea moves quietly without waves, but sometimes it rushes by with terrifying force at speeds up to 200 miles per hour. We already know many of its mysteries. As we seek to explore it, we fear no monsters as did the ancient mariners who first invaded the oceans.

The lower regions of the great sea of air con-tain the clouds, the rainstorms, and snowstorms, and the protective heavy gases which we breathe and which shelter us from the sun's radiation and the wandering meteors.

Above this layer is the stratosphere, thousands of fathoms deep, at the threshold of eternal night where the stars always shine. For countless ages, the stratosphere has been a cold, forbidding, unexplored canopy. But during the past few years, man has ventured into the bottom of the stratosphere—or perhaps we should say the top. He has found the entrance, seven miles above the

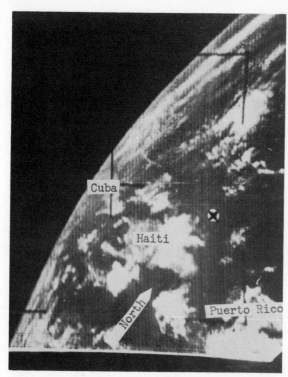

The Caribbean Sea as seen from a Tiros weather satellite whose pictures are flashed to earthbound weathermen by a television transmitter.

surface of our earth, to be guarded by reefs of sparkling emeralds and diamonds beautiful beyond description.

The upper half of the sea of atmosphere is one of violent contrasts and great peril for the new explorers who seek its conquest. Looking at the sun, the astronaut is exposed to the naked force of its brilliance and heat. All other directions are immeasurably cold and dark. Silent, deadly projectiles hurtle by at fantastic speeds. The upper atmosphere contains no living things and can support none. Neither the gilled fish of the ocean nor the plants and animals of the land can live unprotected in this upside-down world halfway between earth and space.

It is within this region, far above the jet trails, that the first skirmishes in the battle to explore other worlds are being fought and won, even though man is capable of survival only in the gentle environment of earth. Flying in space is altogether different from flying in air and it must be approached by taking one difficult and dangerous step at a time.

Two men, Commander M. L. Lewis, of the United States Navy's Bureau of Aeronautics, and Mr. Malcolm D. Ross, of the United States

Office of Naval Research, were among the earliest visitors to the black-vaulted stratosphere. They made their journeys in a shining aluminium gondola attached to a delicate plastic balloon millions of feet in volume but with a skin about half as thick as a single page of this book. These balloons are called *stratolabs* by the scientists and *sky hooks* by most laymen.

During their pioneering voyages, Lewis and Ross invaded only the lower reaches of the stratospheric ocean. Much like the explorers of old, they were forced to go where the strong winds took them.

The gondola provided them with a carefully controlled bubble of the earth-bound lower atmosphere. For further protection, they were dressed in space suits which gave them the appearance of men from another world, which, in a manner of speaking, they were.

The gateway to the stratosphere is reached at about 40,000 feet through a feathery shoal of filmy cirrus clouds. But these clouds are not like those of the lower atmosphere. They are made of ice crystals about the size of wheat grains, floating several inches apart in the thin gases of the outer air.

Often, for several minutes at a time, the stratosphere explorers were becalmed in an iridescent snow storm. The extremely bright sunlight sparkled through the ice crystals giving them the translucent brilliance of precious gems, flashing all the colors of the rainbow. Commander Lewis stated that this part of the trip was like riding through a shower of diamonds, rubies and emeralds, a rain of incalculable riches.

Beyond these sparkling gates lies the threshold of infinity. The stratospheric air is wonderfully clear, uncluttered by earth's waste. The gondola enters a great, inverted bowl whose sides and top are sprinkled with stars against a cobalt background of eternal darkness. The rim turns violet and then is edged with green at the horizon.

For humble man, accustomed to a world of far less contrast, the experience is almost terrifying. He has a dream-like feeling of utter loneliness very much akin to the sensations described by those who have penetrated the still canyons of the ocean deep.

Major David G. Simons of the United States Air Force's Man High Project, which also explored the stratosphere, described the first sunset

A weather satellite picture showing large areas of clouds softly folding over the earth.

and sunrise ever viewed by human eyes from the fringe of space:

"As I sat there in the capsule, my thoughts were interrupted by the most startling, most arresting sight I have ever seen and the one impression of my flight I will carry with me longer than any other: sunset through the pristine clarity of the edge of space.

"It is difficult to communicate its full beauty. Above the distant clouds a thin, reddish, salmon-pink band of atmosphere glowed as the sun edged below the earth's horizon. The salmon glow was crowned by a strip of blue. The color was light and yet intense, as if someone had lifted a veil from an ordinary blue sky to leave it polished and bright. And it was utterly clean, without dust and air to diffuse it. Above, surprisingly, the stars were shining brilliantly.

"Later in the night, I watched a spectacular astral scene. It was Venus setting beyond the earth's horizon. From my vantage point I was looking at the planet through two atmospheres of earth, like the two thicknesses of a glass tumbler when you look through the curved sides. As the light of Venus passed through the bands of atmosphere, the faraway planet twinkled slowly in brilliant colors: first yellow, then green, then red, as if someone were rolling a giant stagelight filter between Venus and my eyes. Each color held for about one second.

"In the morning, I awoke just before the earliest rays of sunrise began to show against the distant horizon. Again I was moved and excited, just as I had been at sunset. I saw a green flash, a typically tropical phenomenon at sunrise and sunset but a sight never before seen this far north. It occurs just as the sun's first direct rays come over the knife-edge of the horizon—a sudden brilliant green flash of light which lasts only for an instant. If I had so much as blinked my eyes, I would have missed it. The flash was followed by the sun's red rays as they shot through the atmosphere. It was beautiful."

In order to report this baroque world of new colors and strange sensations, Major Simons spent 42 hours in the gondola, a good part of it more than 19 miles above the earth's surface.

Others besides Lewis, Ross and Simons have ventured beyond the lower layers of atmosphere, but these pilots have been preoccupied with the necessity of flying neither too fast nor too slow and have had little time to enjoy the view.

The astronauts and cosmonauts are the first living denizens of this earth to survey it with detachment. Not only have they been able to tell

Soft, feathery cirrus clouds race across the sky. These high flying clusters of ice crystals usually accompany good weather.

us much that is new about our own planet, but they will surely be able to solve many mysteries about the others which orbit our sun.

American astronaut John Glenn, aboard the Friendship VII, had this to say about his view of the earth. "As I looked back at the earth from space, colors and light intensities were much the same as I had observed when flying at high altitude in a plane. The colors observed when looking down at the ground appeared similar to those seen from 50,000 feet. When looking toward the horizon, however, the view is completely different, for then the blackness of space contrasts vividly with the brightness of the earth. The horizon itself is a brilliant, brilliant blue and white."

Glenn was the first American to observe four sunsets during the same day, and he remembers this experience quite vividly: "As the sun moves toward the horizon, a black shadow of darkness moves across the earth until the whole surface, except for the bright band at the horizon, is dark. This band is extremely bright just as the sun sets, but as time passes the bottom layer becomes a bright orange and fades into reds, then on into the darker colors, and finally off into the blues and blacks. One thing that surprised me was the distance the light extends on the horizon on each side of the point of the sunset."

According to Colonel Glenn, cloud formations, deserts, and other prominent surface phenomena can be seen clearly from orbital space. He describes thundershowers which he saw on his flight: "Just off the east coast of Africa were two large storm areas. United States Weather Bureau scientists had wondered whether lightning could be seen on the night side, and it certainly can. A large storm was visible just north of my track over the Indian Ocean and a smaller one to the south. Lightning could be seen flashing back and forth between the clouds, but most prominent were lightning flashes within thunderheads illuminating them like light bulbs."

One of the questions being asked by children today is: Where does space begin? Where, indeed? Surely this is a simple question deserving a simple answer.

Unfortunately, each branch of science has its own rules for determining the beginning of space and the end of atmosphere. Biologically, the doorstep is reached for animals at about 100,000 feet. The pressure existing at this altitude causes body fluids to flash into mist. Animal eyes can no longer view even reflected sunlight without protection, and no air is available to be drawn into animal lungs.

The aerodynamicist, who investigates the motions and forces of air and gases on bodies moving through space, is likely to say that space begins at the point where the earth's atmosphere becomes so rarefied that it no longer behaves as a continuous fluid. The aircraft designer has reached outer space when his craft burns up as it seeks to fly fast enough to keep from falling down. For all practical purposes, the weatherman has reached space in the lower layers of the stratosphere. From here outward, his forecasts become monotonously the same: clear and sunny.

The physicists, who are a bit like doctors when it comes to using difficult terms, describe space as a function of the collision-free journey of a molecule. This merely refers to the average or mean distance molecules will travel before they strike others of their kind. At sea level, this mean free path is about a millionth of an inch.

At 70 miles above sea level, molecules will move for more than 50 inches before meeting a friend, and at 250 miles this distance has increased to over 40 miles. We are still not sure what the collision-free path of molecules might be in true outer space, but we know that it is an enormous distance. There are only about 12 molecules per cubic inch in space. Even the best vacuum we have ever been able to create has contained several thousand million molecules per cubic inch.

The life-giving atmosphere not only protects us from lethal radiation and provides us with air, but it also filters out most of what is happening in outer space. Until recently man has been like a deep-sea fish peering upward at the light above,

A NASA manned space shot begins its breathtaking ascent beyond the atmosphere.

only dimly aware of the great universe beyond. The first journeys into space are providing the first clear window to this mysterious outer world.

Where will these journeys take us? Perhaps the closest we can come to a realistic forecast were the words of John Glenn as he left the launching pad in Friendship VII: "The clock is operating . . . We are under way . . . All systems are go."

Cumulus clouds build up quickly over the Grand Canyon.

2. The Majestic Roof of Air

OF ALL THE STRANGE AND WONDERFUL MATERIALS which shape our world, none is more miraculous than the chemical cloak of atmosphere. In the uncounted millions of space miles which they are able to explore, astronomers have discovered that about 90% of cosmic matter exists in the form of the lightest element of all: hydrogen. The rest is mainly helium, the second lightest, while the remaining heavier elements comprise only 2% of the total. Yet pure hydrogen and helium, so plentiful in the universe, are so hard to find in our atmosphere that their presence can be measured only with the greatest difficulty. In an unparalleled reversal of the cosmic trend, the sea of air above us is composed of the dense, rare gases.

How was this unique atmosphere created? And by what celestial vagaries were the vast quantities of hydrogen and helium evaporated from the air around our earth? These riddles have long puzzled astronomers.

Most scientists agree that millions of years ago

an explosion, so vast as to defy comprehension, convulsed our sun; the dust which was later to become the planets showered forth in space to cool. Later, as the worlds began to form, the baby earth's gravitational field was too weak to retain the lighter gases and these were boiled away into outer space by the mighty heat of the young sun. Then, through the long, dark millennia before the emergence of life, the heavier gases imprisoned beneath the cooling crust of the earth bubbled forth. These were methane, nitrogen, and some carbon dioxide. The earth breathed them out through cracks, volcanoes, and the dark rifts in its shell. Each discharge nurtured the thin atmosphere, and the impenetrable darkness of space was replaced by a sky already turning blue. Clouds formed and torrential rains lashed the primeval crust to gather in hollows and so start the oceans. The first bacteria acted upon the methane to convert it miraculously into carbon dioxide. Algae covered the seas with a thin, persistent scum and released oxygen by the mysterious process of photosynthesis. The cycle of life had begun.

Thus, the rudimentary beginnings of life initiated the evolution of our present atmosphere, and the decay of early plants and the excreta of the first animals continued slowly to build the medium of air within which we survive and flourish. These processes replenish the atmosphere today just as the rivers replenish the sea; the air has become a growing medium with a composition varied and controlled by the evolutionary trends of the life it supports with such bountiful care.

When man became aware of the evolutionary process, he assumed that the sea had mothered the first life. This assumption developed naturally, since most living things are composed largely of liquid. The blood of man exhibits many characteristics of sea water; it is salty and contains most of the same elements. Furthermore, the oceans form a soft, protective medium with an even temperature very suitable for the first, viscous growth. Today, however, a good case can be developed to show that life originated, not in the sea of water, but in the sea of air.

Most biologists agree that the first life probably existed as a complex protein molecule with one unusual attribute which differentiated it from all which had come and gone before: it could absorb

other molecules and duplicate itself from their materials. Such organic molecules possessed the two basic requisites of life: they grew and they reproduced themselves.

The building blocks from which the complex protein molecules evolve are the amino acids. For some years, scientists suspected that these could be made in the laboratory by duplicating conditions similar to those found in the earth's first primitive atmosphere. In the United States, Dr. Harold Urey and his associates once conducted an experiment to test this theory. They constructed a test-tube earth with the same characteristics which existed on our planet millions of years ago when life began. The atmosphere of this test-tube earth was composed of methane, ammonia, and hydrogen. Water which contained the same minerals as the primitive oceans was placed in the tube. Then the system was sealed and the water heated until a mist, resembling that of the ancient clouds, formed. Small electrodes energized the circulating gases, producing a bombardment very similar to that of the powerful radiation beamed forth by the immature sun which streamed down through the first atmosphere.

The system was allowed to steam its prehistoric brew for a week. Then it was disconnected and the contents were analyzed. Definite amounts of three amino acids were found, proving that these complex substances which exist in living tissue could have been created in the earth's original atmosphere by chemical reaction.

Dr. Urey and his associates do not claim to have created life in their test-tube earth, nor do

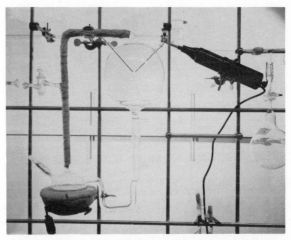

The "test-tube" earth provided an atmosphere similar to that of primitive worlds.

11

By a freak of nature, snow falls in a tropical land and palm trees rise above the snow-covered ground at Tlemcen, Algeria.

they entirely understand the process by which the evolution of organic matter took place. However, their findings do indicate that such processes could exist. Had it been possible to provide in the test tube all the probabilities of the vast ocean of air, and had it been practicable to maintain it for an indefinitely long period, we might have seen a replica of the first life-molecule come creeping up the evolutionary stairs.

Perhaps these life-molecules were thus born in the clouds above the planet, spawned in the turbulence of the lightning and the wind. Later they were rained upon the earth and, like all things, ultimately washed into the sea. Once within that mother bosom, they grew and evolved and multiplied until the oceans were teeming with them and life was firmly anchored upon the periphery of this globe. The sea life grew to invade the land; from this molecular beginning countless life-forms took shape. Yet all were bound by one common element: the atmosphere which nourished them.

For each scientist, our atmosphere holds a separate interest. The chemist sees it as a source of raw materials—nitrates for explosives and oxides for solvents—a chemical warehouse, inexhaustible with the accumulations of history. The meteorologist—or weather scientist—is concerned with it as the sun's partner in weather-making. To the aerodynamicist, the atmosphere is a fluid medium of travel like the surface of the sea. According to the space engineer it is a prison. Inevitably, each of the specialists in our sciences finds in the atmosphere a factor to affect his calculations.

But we need not be scientists to be aware of the wonders our atmosphere creates for us. If some miracle made it possible to survive without breathing, how strange would be our awakening in an airless world: With no alarm clock to prompt us, we would awaken to a stillness complete and absolute. The world would be soundless without the air to carry the pressure waves which vibrate against our eardrums. Breakfast would be a cold, dismal meal because no fire would burn. We would walk to our schools and our work since motor cars would not run without oxygen to ignite their fuel. The sky would be a dark, cobalt blue; the stars cold and unwinking beside the rising sun. There would be neither predawn light nor sunset without an atmosphere to refract the sun's rays. There would be no wind and no clouds —no weather at all except heat and cold. Meteors would hurtle down from outer space to scar our cities without warning, untroubled by the atmospheric friction which causes them to burn themselves out before reaching the surface of the earth.

We would acquire a new standard for temperature. After a bitterly cold night, the day would soon become unbearably hot as the thermometer rose swiftly above the boiling point of

12

water. We should be forced to seek shelter from the sun, because the protective cloak of atmosphere would no longer be present to guard us from its killing cosmic rays.

These are but the barest few of the changes which would be encountered in an airless world. The most spectacular effects probably would be produced by the elimination of atmospheric pressure. Car tires would swell up to several times normal size; many would burst. Our bodies would feel the tremendous effect of this decreased pressure which would release nitrogen into the bloodstream and thus make us victims of the deep-sea diver's disease called bends. Our skins would distend and stretch much like those of the deep-sea fish hauled to the sea's surface.

Only the astronomers would feel happier about our lost atmosphere, assuming they lived long enough to rejoice. Without the blurring cloak of air which, even on the best nights, distorts the images of the stars, they could solve many of the perplexing mysteries of the cosmic depths. They would quickly unravel the tantalizing question of the canals on Mars as they searched through an airless space. Many unknown galaxies would gleam pure and clear before their amazed eyes and perhaps the full extent of the universe could finally be measured.

In reality, the airless world would be a grim one. We would be tortured by unbearable heat in the daytime and incredible cold at night. Painfully huddled against our airless and soundless earth, we would be doomed. Almost immediately all life would cease on this globe.

This atmosphere, which provides the life-giving oxygen for our lungs, exhibits awesome characteristics. It towers above us to form an ocean of gases hundreds of miles high. As the blind deep-sea fish must bear the ocean pressures, so must we of earth's surface bear the weight of the gaseous sea. It presses down on our bodies with the crushing force of more than 14 pounds per square inch. The narrow column of air which rests on our shoulders alone weighs almost 2,000 pounds. We are so marvellously constituted that we do not even notice this. Nor do we often realize, as do our aircraft designers, that air has mass and weight. If we could empty the air in our living room into a milk can and weigh it, this "milk" would weigh 400 pounds.

The deep blanket of air is not of the same con-

These weathermen are preparing to take soundings of the upper atmosphere. Behind the observer's shed is a radar antenna used to track the balloon on its upward flight. Measurements of the upper air are taken several times each day at most weather stations.

sistency at all levels, but instead is built more like a four-layer cake, each layer having its individual characteristics.

The region immediately above the earth's surface is called the *troposphere*. This is the heaviest and, to us, far the most meaningful part of our atmosphere. It accounts for three-fourths of the entire weight of air and contains substantially all the water mist and carbon dioxide. Within the troposphere, temperature falls about three degrees for each additional 1,000 feet of altitude; this region acts as a warm blanket to moderate the terrible extremes of outer space.

The area between the troposphere and the next layer above is called the *tropopause*. The average height of this boundary varies from about 25,000 feet above the earth's poles to over 50,000 feet at the equator. Along the tropopause lie strong high-velocity currents of air called the jet streams. These Olympian wind tunnels have a profound effect upon our surface weather, and will be discussed fully in a later chapter.

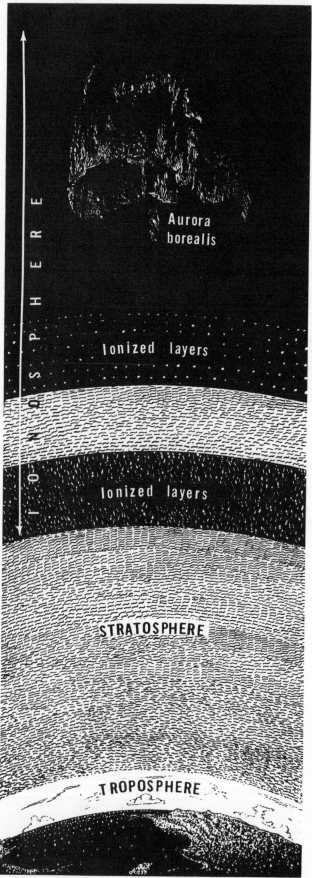

The multi-layered atmosphere with aurora borealis above.

The second layer of air above the earth is the *stratosphere*. This portion of the atmospheric blanket contributes about 24% of the total weight. Normally we would expect that the farther we proceed out to the absolute cold of space, the lower the temperature. This is not true in the stratosphere. Temperature is practically iso-thermal (the same) through the first 25 miles. Then, mysteriously, it begins to increase from 67° below zero to 170° above.

The uppermost portion of the stratosphere is called the *ozonosphere*, and it absorbs a considerable portion of the deadly cosmic radiation from the sun.

In the thin, soundless reaches above the stratosphere lies the third layer, the *ionosphere*. The limits of both the upper and lower regions of this area are subject to wide daily and seasonal variations. The presence of the ionosphere was predicted by two electronic scientists named Kennelly and Heaviside in an attempt to explain the unique reception of radio waves noted by early operators. The ionosphere is so named because of the large number of ions which are present (ions are positively charged atoms which have lost some of their electrons). These mongrel atoms cause peculiar reflections of radio and radar waves which produce many unusual effects. When the ionosphere is disturbed by sunspots—which have a great influence upon its composition—we experience considerable radio interference in the form of static. Temperature in the ionosphere falls sharply from 170° to −27° and then increases rapidly to about 4,000°.

The outermost level of atmosphere, the *exosphere*, theoretically has a lower limit somewhere between 300 and 600 miles above the earth. Like the other layers, its boundaries are subject to many variations. The air is so thin in this layer that the molecules are widely separated; many of them break away from the earth's magnetic field and become space travellers on their own. Because of this molecular wandering, there is no sharp upper limit to the exosphere. It is like steam which rises from a tropical jungle and gradually disappears. Because of our nearness to the sun, the temperature remains about 4,000° throughout the layer. The cold of outer space is bottomless, near absolute zero (−273.7°C.).

Through the first 50 miles of outward travel, the chemical composition of the atmosphere re-

During a polar night at a Russian gas works, the cold and desolate earth is brightened by burning fumes.

mains constant, with a ratio of four parts of nitrogen to one part of oxygen. Beyond 50 miles, molecular oxygen separates into individual atoms; at 200 miles the same thing happens to nitrogen. Within the upper regions of the exosphere, only hydrogen and helium are present.

Although we have long been curious about our sea of air, the science of its study is relatively new and a great many questions remain to be answered. We are puzzled and know very little about the upper atmosphere, particularly with regard to the reaction of the atmosphere under the constant bombardment of solar radiation. Because of this and other reasons, we have so far been restricted in our flight to the lower regions. But we are not satisfied, and scientists are busy launching unmanned rockets to probe metallic fingers into the atmospheric brew and bring back information which will enable us to go still a little higher.

We do know that the multi-layered atmosphere, in addition to protecting us, also provides our weather. Both of these duties are closely related, as we shall see.

The most important effect of the atmosphere upon weather is caused by the penetration of the sun's rays. The great bubble around our earth provides us with a built-in air conditioner known as the *Greenhouse Effect*, which allows the atmosphere to act as a trap for the sun's energy. Solar radiation comes to us in relatively short waves which easily penetrate our atmosphere. Upon striking the earth, these rays are transformed into the long waves of heat. The atmosphere, so generously allowing the short rays to penetrate, acts as a covering blanket against the longer waves and thus prevents loss of heat by radiation. This heat, which is collected in the air and upon the surface of the earth, supplies both the warmth necessary to support life and the energy to motivate storms and weather changes. It is the main basis for the statement that all our energy comes from the sun.

Another important rôle of the atmosphere in relation to weather is the transportation of water mist. The air around the earth contains an average total of 17,000,000,000,000 tons of moisture. If this gigantic load were dumped suddenly upon the surface of an area as large as the United States, it would cover that country with a blanket of water more than seven feet deep. Fortunately, nature has provided a more orderly distribution in the form of rain and snow. This precipitation is

15

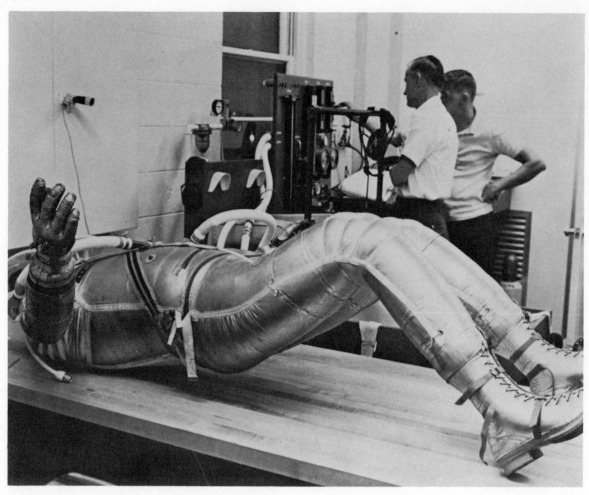

This pressure suit is an astronaut's way of taking his atmosphere with him.

part of the cycle by which water is siphoned from the sea to replenish the flow of our rivers and irrigate our farms.

As an example, the warm breezes blowing north from the Gulf of Mexico carry vaporized moisture inland for great distances. When this mist is condensed and deposited by rainstorms, it eventually drains into the Mississippi River and flows back into the Gulf again. The worldwide result is like a gigantic, endless conveyor-belt by means of which water is brought to the land.

As modern technology has advanced, the frontiers of science have moved up into the atmosphere and the nebulous void which lies beyond. Each year the space probes penetrate higher and higher. The German V-2 rockets and the United States Navy's early Vikings have been replaced by the latest in rockets and space vehicles under the United States Mercury and Gemini projects. The Russians also have similar vehicles. We have already crossed the threshold of a new era. Space

travel, no more than a wild dream a decade ago, has become a reality.

But the earth's atmosphere is also man's prison. Many barriers remain to be crossed before we can live without the support of its protective features. Space travel is more than a matter of transportation; it is a matter of reproducing life's environment in capsule, self-replenishing form.

Any human probing into space must begin with conquest of the atmosphere, for air is to us as sea is to fish. The ocean surface is the roof of the shark's world, and the lowest atmospheric layer, the troposphere, has been the ceiling on man through all past ages. Going out farther requires that we take with us a bubble of the atmospheric temperature, pressure, and elements within which we are mortally bound.

Long before man had entered the stratosphere, he realized that he would need a space suit that could duplicate atmospheric pressure and temperature, and thus be a sort of portable environment. The United States Navy developed the first such outfit, known as the *Gorilla Suit* to the uncomfortable airmen who were required to wear it. The Gorilla Suit was designed on the same principle as a car tire. The pilot is simply encased in a huge rubber suit which is inflated to atmospheric pressure. Unfortunately, his arms and legs then become almost immobile, making it most difficult for him to work or even move.

A second type of suit was designed for the United States Air Force, but it has not proved to be ideal, either. This item is called the *partial pressure suit* for the very good reason that it does not fully compensate for the loss of atmosphere. However, a pilot wearing it might be able to stay alive for about ten minutes in a vacuum. The partial pressure suit must be individually fitted. It consists of a very tight covering with long tubes of cloth leading to the arms and legs. Upon loss of atmospheric pressure, these pipes are filled with high pressure air which tightens the suit so that enough pressure is maintained to keep the body fluids from vaporizing. The hands and neck, which are not pressurized, become swollen and painful after a few moments. This suit is used as a safety device and is not relied upon as a permanent means of surviving on the edge of space.

Colonel John Glenn was safely encased in a modified version of the Gorilla Suit during his epic three-orbit flight around the earth on February 20, 1962. Each of the American astronauts has one of these suits which has been especially tailored for him. Many improvements have been made to the original design. A pressure seal, for example, has been provided around the astronaut's wrists so that his hands can be used to better advantage. Miniature needlelike red finger lights are attached to the index and middle fingers of both gloves. These are powered by batteries on the back of the gloves and they provide illumination so that the astronaut can read his instruments as he passes from daylight to darkness. In order to ensure that the astronaut's life is a comfortable one at all times when he is in space, a portable, lightweight ventilator system is available to provide suit cooling when he is not attached to the artificial atmosphere of the space capsule.

In addition to the artificial atmosphere provided by his space suit, the astronaut carries with him a second man-made climate which is contained by the space capsule itself. The tempera-

Colonel John Glenn enters "Friendship VII" for his epic voyage in space.

ture and pressure of the cabin are about the same as those of the suit so that the astronaut can survive if either one fails.

The efficiency of the temperature control system is one of the true miracles of modern science. During re-entry, the air within the astronaut's space suit is held at a temperature of about 85°. Only a few inches away, on the surface of the heat shield, the temperature rises as high as 3,000°! During orbit, the outside skin temperature of the capsule may vary from 200° to −50°. Inside his space suit, the astronaut carries out his chores at a comfortable 65° to 75°.

Astronaut John Glenn had this to say about the temperature control within Friendship VII: "I did not feel particularly hot until we were getting down to about 80,000 to 75,000 feet. From there on I was uncomfortably warm and by the time the main parachute was out I was perspiring profusely." During this period of maximum heating, the retropack was burning up and flying by Glenn's observation window. The heat shield glowed with an orange color, so great was the heat of friction.

Since all our thoughts are geared to the conditions existing on the earth's surface, it is hard for us to appreciate the hazards of high-altitude flight. As an example, tests show that a pilot suddenly exposed to the low pressure encountered at

The panorama of clouds, curvature of the earth and black sky photographed from a V-2 rocket in the outer reaches of space show the lower troposphere layer of the atmosphere as a thin, delicately formed haze on the horizon. Cumulus clouds are forming over the mountain ridges near the river basin.

a height of 25,000 feet loses consciousness within three or four minutes. This has given rise to a new concept called useful consciousness. An aviator's useful consciousness decreases rapidly with height. At 30,000 feet it is one minute; at 50,000 feet it has dropped to about 15 seconds. In the space of the astronauts, man has no useful consciousness once he is exposed to the elements.

Why do we lose consciousness at high altitudes?

The reason is a graphic illustration of our dependence upon the atmosphere. At 50,000 feet the outside air pressure has fallen to the air pressure inside human lungs. Since the diaphragm acts as a bellows to produce this low pressure and thus draw air into the lungs, there is no manner whereby a human can breathe above 50,000 feet in the free atmosphere, and man becomes exactly like a fish out of water. He gasps futilely as his lungs exhaust the air in them and can obtain no more. Within 15 seconds, the oxygen stored in the brain tissues is reduced to the point at which consciousness is lost. In the light of these facts, the need for a space suit which will accommodate itself to pressure changes and insure an adequate oxygen supply is quite apparent.

The first man to journey to the planets will become the loneliest creature of all time. Beyond his own atmosphere, he is an alien venturer into an unfamiliar and terrifying environment. Because of inherent physical ties with his own world,

there is no other known planet on which he can survive. This fact is illustrated by the following table which provides some comparative data on the atmospheres of the nearby planets which will be explored early in the conquest of space.

Planet	Approximate Temperature	Surface Pressure (Lb. per sq. in.)	Atmospheric Elements
Venus	122° to −212°	2.3	Nitrogen, carbon dioxide
Earth	50°	14.7	Nitrogen, water, oxygen, argon, carbon dioxide
Mars	0°	.20	Nitrogen, water, carbon dioxide, argon
Jupiter	−184°	.75	Hydrogen, methane, helium, ammonia
Saturn	−238°	.75	Same as Jupiter

One of the striking features revealed by this table is the lack of oxygen on other planets. This is one reason why space travellers must take their own atmosphere with them, and why any permanent habitation of other worlds must remain a future dream. Generally speaking, the smaller planets, such as Venus, Earth, Mercury and Mars, have atmospheres which contain such heavy gases as nitrogen, carbon dioxide, argon, and water mist. The larger planets, Jupiter and

Saturn, have atmospheres composed of the lighter gases: hydrogen, ammonia, helium, and methane.

Meteorology applied to other planets is a relatively new science. The object of such study is not only to supply information for future space travellers but also to learn more about the atmosphere of the earth, since certain atmospheric factors are better viewed from the outside looking in.

Mars is the planet which most resembles the earth in climate and composition. Since it is also the closest, the surface and surrounding gases have been studied eagerly by both astronomers and weathermen using the latest astronomical tools.

Schiaparelli, the Italian astronomer, startled the 19th-century world when he published his discovery of the famous canals of Mars in 1877. The early part of this century witnessed many studies of Mars, and considerable debate resulted. It soon became apparent that an intricate spider-web of lines was faintly visible on the best nights through large telescopes. They could be seen only by certain astronomers with exceptional vision. Many scientists doubted their existence altogether, while others considered them no more than surface cracks.

About one definite discovery, however, there could be no possible doubt: The polar regions of Mars display a glittering whiteness which waxes and wanes with the changing seasons. Percival Lowell, who founded an observatory with the express purpose of studying the planet, insisted that the colors of the canals changed in intensity during the year. He believed that the canals became more pronounced as the polar icecaps

faded away. His theory, coupled with the controversy over the canals themselves, led to widespread speculation about the possibility of life on our adjacent planet.

Modern instruments have provided only a few of the answers to the riddle of Mars. The atmosphere contains three distinct layers. From 6 to 20 miles above the surface, there appears a stratum of thin blue-white clouds; these seem to be made of fine ice crystals. Between a height of three and six miles there exists a thin violet haze which seems to be composed of either ice crystals or water mist. Just above the surface are yellow clouds of dust and sand.

The 1965 Mariner IV epic voyage has unravelled a number of Martian puzzles which had mystified astronomers for centuries. Previously, they had thought the red planet's air was thin, perhaps like that of a 10-mile-high mountain peak, but as Mariner passed behind the planet the small changes in its transmitted radio waves suggested an even more rarefied atmospheric cloak. It now appears that Mars has an atmospheric equivalent to that of an earth mountain almost 20 miles high!

However, large areas of the red planet are often surrounded by dust storms and, because of the rarefied nature of the air, the atmosphere must be extremely turbulent, producing extremely high winds to raise the surface dust. Solar radiation, such as deadly cosmic rays, is not shielded by a thick canopy like that which protects the earth. This also makes the environment of Mars difficult but probably not impossible for life as we know it.

One problem for future astronauts heralded by Mariner IV is caused by the thin Martian atmosphere. Previously it had been thought that

The sun's family of planets are separated by millions of miles.

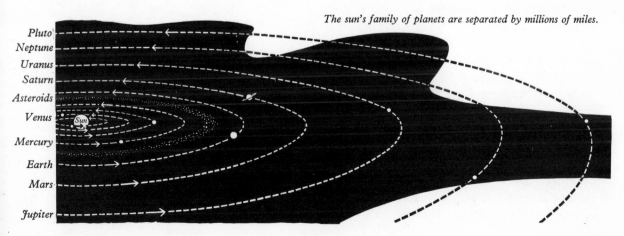

Pluto
Neptune
Uranus
Saturn
Asteroids
Venus
Mercury
Earth
Mars
Jupiter
Sun

"soft" landings could be made on the planet by means of parachutes, but the Martian atmosphere is too rare. The first earth visitors of both robots and men will probably have to be lowered to the surface using retro-rockets, a costly and weight-consuming method of landing.

On Mars, the temperature varies with the season and latitude just as it does on earth. However, Mars is farther away from the sun, and the average daily temperature hovers near zero. The atmosphere is very thin, at the surface being equivalent to that about 100,000 feet above the earth. This reduces the Martian Greenhouse Effect, and the daily temperature extremes are much greater. At noon on a summer day, the temperature will rise to 100° at the equator; the same night, it drops to −30°. Two-thirds of the surface is covered by a reddish, arid desert. The polar icecaps are thin, with an average depth of less than one foot. As they melt, a dusky blue color spreads over portions of the planet. The same hue has been reproduced by sunlight reflected from certain lichens and mosses found on the earth. The new space-based observatories may provide additional facts about Mars, but most astronomers are now convinced that there is no animal life as we know it on the planet.

Venus is nearest the earth in size, but because of its proximity to the sun, we know little about its atmosphere. Venus rotates very slowly; one day on the planet is equal to three weeks on the earth. There are only small amounts of water mist in its atmosphere and almost 500 times more carbon dioxide than is present around the earth. Observed atmospheric clouds are believed to be composed mainly of dust.

Meteorologically speaking, Jupiter and Saturn are very mysterious. They both have definite dark belts and light zones parallel to their equators. Jupiter has a dense, swirling atmosphere composed largely of methane and ammonia gases with traces of hydrogen and helium. Examination of this atmosphere is limited to the upper levels which contain huge, opaque clouds which obscure the surface below. A gigantic, mysteriously crimson oval 30,000 miles long and 7,000 miles wide, called the Great Red Spot, is located near the equator. This phenomenon has been observed in the same position for the last 70 years. The spot is explained by scientists as being a disturbance in Jupiter's upper atmosphere similar to the great cyclonic storms recently discovered about 30,000 feet above the earth. Most astronomers believe that these upper air storms would appear as white patches to observers from other planets.

Through these studies of the atmosphere and weather of other planets, we hope to search out the secrets of our own air-envelope and thus prepare for the day when man emerges from his planetary cocoon. Most of the facts explained in this chapter were unknown at the beginning of the century; many of them were understood imperfectly as late as 15 years ago. Even today some of the fundamental relationships within our atmosphere are mysteries. But there is constant progress, and the curtain is lifting so rapidly that the face of our world seems constantly to change. As we venture farther into space, the next few years will certainly produce greater understanding of our atmosphere and its functions. Perhaps the fruits of this knowledge will enable us to harness the roof of air and make it do our bidding just as we now are learning to control the atom. For there is no conquest so unattainable, no scientific advance so awesome that man does not dream of achieving it some day.

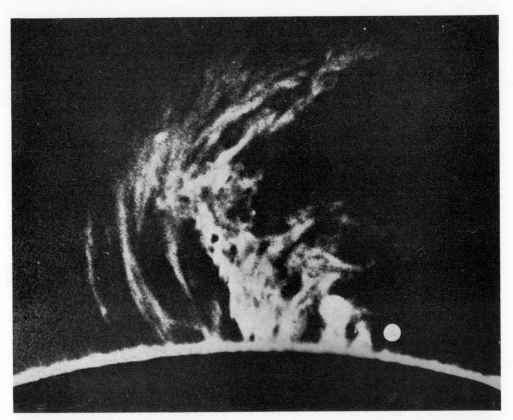

These gigantic flames, reaching outward more than 100,000 miles from the rim of the sun, furnish all the light and heat for the solar system. The small white circle at the lower right shows the relative size of the earth.

3. The Atomic Furnace

THE OCEAN OF ATMOSPHERE WHICH SURROUNDS US has provided a canopy over the earth for untold ages. It would appear logical that this sea of air would long ago have stabilized into a soft, still envelope so that now there would be no thunderstorms, no sudden gales, no lashing rain. The reasons why this is not so are simple, although they puzzled man for many centuries. It is only lately that we have become aware that our atmosphere is like soup steaming in a gigantic kettle, churned and boiled by the radiant heat from our sun.

Man lives crablike, near the surface of his sphere, imprisoned in a delicately balanced medium between two fires. The panoramic sweep of heaven which enfolds his spinning globe simmers at an ambient 4,000°, hot enough to melt the finest tempered steel. His tentative probing at the earth underneath him finds the temperature rising sharply over the boiling point of water at depths of two miles. Deeper still at 30 miles it leaps to 2,000°, and the central core where ancient men assigned the damned for eternity is a molten mass boiling at 10,000°. It is only within the narrow skin of union between earth and sky that the temperature and the elements miraculously combine to form an environment which permits his existence.

But the temperature variations which lie above and below us, extreme though they be, are minor

21

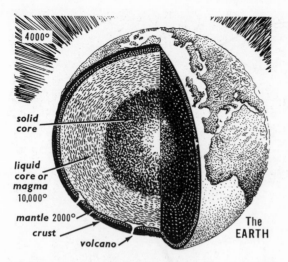

solid
core

liquid
core or
magma
10,000°

mantle 2000°

crust

volcano

4000°

The
EARTH

The inner core of our earth is extremely dense and very hot.

compared with the mighty heat of our sun. Most of us have not yet seen—and we hope will never see—the explosion of an atomic bomb, yet daily we watch the hydrogen bomb at work. For the sun is a vast ball of just such explosions as we are now attempting to create in our laboratories. These eruptions are of gigantic power and terrible efficiency, shooting flames more than 150,000 miles into space. They are the result of the energy released by the conversion of hydrogen into helium. The tremendous heat generated by this transformation produces a surface temperature of 10,000° and an estimated 20,000,000° inside the sun, lighting the planets and providing warmth so that the thin green film of life can survive on the periphery of this earth.

When Einstein established the equivalence of mass and energy, he ushered in an age during which many startling facts have become evident. The sun, for example, daily radiates an enormous quantity of energy. Since energy and mass are mutually convertible, the solar radiation corresponds to a weight loss in the sun of nearly 5,000,000 tons per second. The earth absorbs 150 tons of this mass each day. The sun has been burning for more than 2,000,000,000 years, but it is so vast that only one-tenth of its hydrogen has been lost in this energy-making process. At the present rate, it will be another 18,000,000,000 years before the big light goes out.

The sun is the great architect of life. This can be seen in the mute testimony of the flowers as they turn their faces hourly to the warm, life-giving rays while the sun sweeps around the earth's curve. It can be seen in the abundance and vitality of life which reaches skyward under the direct heat of the tropical sun near the equator. It is felt within man himself as he seeks the warm sunlit climates during the cold winter months. And although the necessities of living mechanisms are many, none are so vital as those given out by the sun. Its energy provides the vehicle by which plants "digest" their food; its warmth maintains the delicate balance of temperature which allows the existence of the flesh of animals and the liquid state of water.

But with all his realization of its importance, man understands the workings of the sun hardly at all. Until the beginning of the 20th century scientists thought that the sun was merely in the process of cooling after having been heated by the mighty primordial flame of creation. But the energy equations available today show that such a lifeless body would lose its power to radiate heat in approximately 3,000 years. Since the geological time clocks found on the earth's face prove that the sun has lighted the world for many millions of years, the cooling theory was discarded. Now most scientists agree that the sun's energy must come from that which is stored within the atom.

As man peers at the sun through his astronomical tools, the telescope and the spectrohelioscope, he finds many things which still puzzle him. There are vast, whirling storms which fill his eyes with wonder. He can photograph the great solar prominences which erupt violently, sending fingerlike streamers of flame far out into space, and he sees the gigantic dark spots which often grow to sizes much larger than this earth. But the reasons behind these and other solar phenomena elude him. He knows that the sun is millions of degrees hot, but the highest temperature he has been able to generate in his laboratories is in the order of 12,000°, and the effect of this solar heat upon the structure and composition of matter remains far beyond his present knowledge.

The mighty pressures existing within the molten shell of the sun are measured in thousands of tons per square inch. But the greatest pressures man can generate approach these only as a grain of sand approaches the desert. The vast core must be liquid because no material known or imagined could exist as a solid in such intense heat. But this liquid is like no other liquid within the limits of our experience, for the extreme pressure at

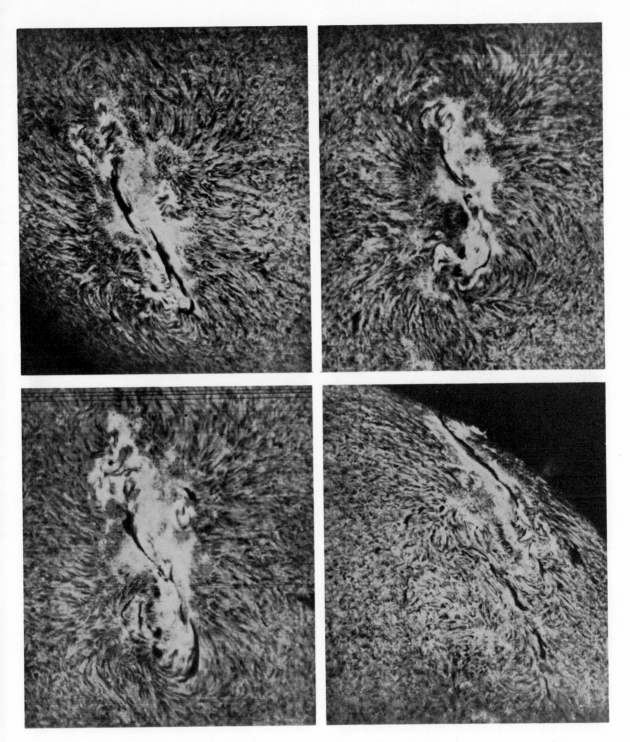

Sunspots are believed to be violent storms on the sun's surface.

the core could crush the molecules of all substances into a density far beyond anything we know. We can only guess at the changes this produces in the basic atomic structure of matter since it is not within our present abilities to investigate them.

If observers from other celestial systems know of our existence at all, it is only because of the radiated light from our beacon sun. The energy it releases permeates all the planets of the solar system and extends beyond them to the outer reaches of space to become a true link with infinity.

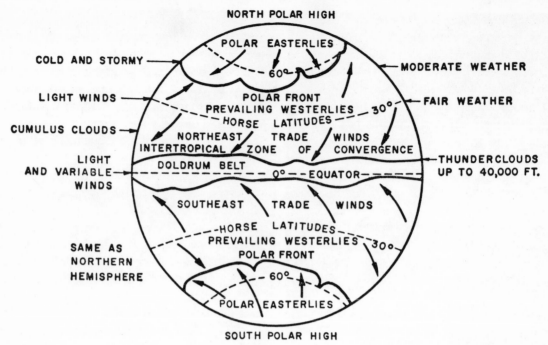

The global circulation of air provides an infinite pattern of change and variety, bringing rain, sun, warmth and cold to refresh our world.

The powerful effects of this radiant energy, unevenly absorbed by our planet, together with the rotation of the earth produce the great circulation patterns of the atmosphere and are the basic cause of all our weather.

The key to an understanding of weather phenomena lies in a knowledge of these circulation patterns. They are produced, not by the sun alone, but also by the rotating earth; however, in order to simplify the picture, let us first assume that the earth is stationary. Thus we will be able to see clearly just what effect the radiation of the sun has upon our atmosphere.

The earth's rotation has suddenly stopped, and the sun appears stationary at a point above the equator. Most of the heat from its rays is absorbed by the atmosphere midway between the poles, and this causes the air near the equator to become much hotter than that of the poles. The hot air rises, producing low-pressure areas at the equator, and the cold dense air from the extremities of our sphere rushes in to fill the gap. Warmed by the equatorial heat, this air also expands and must rise. The result is a gigantic, invisible Ferris wheel of atmosphere which circulates towards the equator on the surface and away from it at high altitudes. As the upper air flows away from the sun, it is cooled and becomes heavy, causing a downward flow at the poles. Thus

the cycle is complete, and the atmosphere is continually on the move, aerating our world, shifting constantly over the land, a flow without beginning and without end, enduring beyond time.

The rotating earth superimposes on these basic north-south air currents another and more complex flow. As the earth rotates, so does its atmosphere. And since outer space is wholly frictionless, the mass of atmosphere keeps pace with earth. At the equator, the earth's circumference is large, almost 25,000 miles. Thus the air at the equator turns through 25,000 miles of space each day. Since the earth likewise moves at this speed, there is little or no surface wind at the equator.

As the tropical air, heated by the sun, rises to take its long northward path to the poles, it maintains this rotary speed. But as it moves north, the earth's circumference rapidly grows less, and the earth's surface speed diminishes proportionately. Hence, as the equatorial air travels northward, it moves faster than the surface below, and the middle latitude winds are born. These winds seem to rise in the east and for this reason they are called *easterlies*. In this manner, the north-south winds produced by the sun's heat are twisted unevenly to the west, and the winds of the earth blow askew across her surface.

These simple patterns become enormously complicated because of the earth's surface characteristics. Some areas absorb more heat than others. Mountain ranges deflect the winds into scattered shards. Winds en route to the poles at high altitudes lose their heat, sink, and form swirling eddies with the surface streams below.

A complete discussion of the earth's flow patterns is far too complicated for this book, but the effects are interesting. At the equator the breezes are light, and the pressure is relatively low. This belt is called the *doldrums* and was shunned by the weather-wise captains of sailing vessels in ancient times. In parallel bands on either side of the equator are the twin belts of easterlies known as the *trade winds*. They were a boon to many generations of mariners who plied the seas from Europe in their sailing vessels searching for commerce in the New World. Above the trades lie the *prevailing westerlies*, currents of the temperate latitudes where most of our weather is brewed. The frigid *polar easterlies* chill the ends of the earth and complete the general circulation pattern.

To an observer in space, the earth would appear ringed with wind bands, flowing alternately east and west—a planetary barber-pole.

Our visitor in the space suit would be quick to observe that in two localities, one just under the polar easterlies and the other at the equator, opposing flow systems meet. These boundary regions are called *fronts*—the *polar front* and the *inter-tropical zone of convergence* or *equatorial front*. Both are low-pressure areas created by the ascension of surface-heated air to higher altitudes, and both are characterized by storminess and bad weather. The United States and Europe are primarily concerned with the polar front. The waves and nodes which form in it during the winter months invade the temperate zone to produce most of their cold weather.

The radiant power of the sun, beating down on a polished earth, would produce the circulation effects we have noted. But the earth is not a mirror which reflects the sun's radiation uniformly. The great oceans absorb and store the automatically generated heat and act as a giant thermostat to dampen changes of temperature in our atmosphere. Sea currents carry tropical heat to wash lands which would otherwise be snow-encrusted. Half our world owes its mild climate to the heat-charged Gulf Stream. The land, the mountains, the valleys and the low, level plains—each mirrors the sun's energy differently and so shapes the local climate.

The earth's varying geography thus alters the balance of temperature throughout the world. Most of the land and the highest mountain ranges lie in the Northern Hemisphere. This unbalanced distribution, coupled with the fact that three-fourths of earth's surface is covered by water,

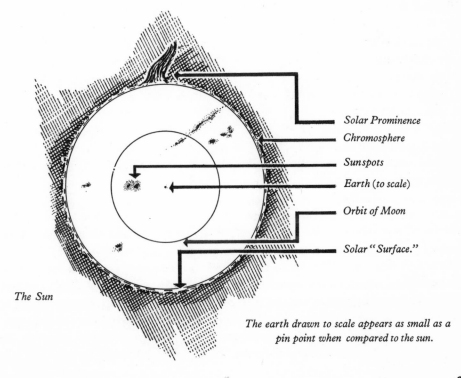

The Sun

Solar Prominence
Chromosphere
Sunspots
Earth (to scale)
Orbit of Moon
Solar "Surface."

*The earth drawn to scale appears as small as a
pin point when compared to the sun.*

produces major temperature changes. If the earth were an ideal sphere, the North and South Poles would be the coldest regions. In the Southern Hemisphere this is almost correct. However, the northern cold pole is located in Siberia, almost one-third the distance down to the equator.

The heat equator, or band of hottest temperature, varies with the path of the sun. Generally it is attracted northward by the continents. During the summer months it extends into the United States through the California valleys and sometimes almost up to the Oregon border—40% of the distance to the pole.

The net result of coalescing sun, atmosphere, rotation, and geography is inconsistency and fluctuation. Although the steady, ageless sun is the prime mover of our weather, it is forever different and unpredictable. Yet miraculously these weather variations are but the merest ripples in the galactic scale and always remain within the incredibly thin limits necessary to foster the fragile, jelly-like growth of life upon our planet.

As the day starts with the sun and sets with the sun, so does all else. The total influence of the sun upon the earth is today only partially understood and dimly realized. If it were not for the circulation of the atmosphere caused by the great lamp's heat, huge pools of oxygen would stagnate over the jungles near the equator. Without the controls provided by the flowing air, large areas of the earth would become unbearably cold or terribly hot. We know little of the cosmic radiation in its pure form; but that little links its energy units directly into the basic life processes.

There are many possibilities which may bring an end to life on this globe: A new chemical in the gaseous envelope of atmosphere; a single mutation in a presently unremarkable microbe; a sudden shift in the delicately balanced gravitational field—any of these might sweep the living world away. But thereafter, new life would grow as the sun moved northward for the next spring. Only when the cinder grows cold, only when morning comes with no warmth and no light will the world be truly dead. And on that blank and patternless day when the sun dies, then only can we say with certainty that the zero cold of timeless death will settle on the face of this earth.

A formidable line of thunderstorms with majestic anvil tops hovers over a bustling city.

4. Islands in the Sky

THE GREAT WIND PATTERNS OF THE EARTH HAVE been known and used by men for many centuries. Since these air currents carry our weather with them, it is surprising that the tricks and variations of the global weather patterns baffled the human mind for so many generations.

The problem persisted primarily because of false beliefs rather than false weather observations. The early weather prophets believed, reasonably enough, that the canopy of air covered the earth with a uniform, protective blanket having the same characteristics at the equator and the poles. Weather was assumed to be a local phenomenon and many false trails were generated in the search for the weather-producing elements. Primitive peoples explained weather even more simply. It was a form of punishment or reward visited upon them by the deities. Good weather came from benevolent, happy gods; storm and drought meant that these overlords were angry. The beating of drums and the offering of sacrifices were the best way of appeasing their wrath and changing the weather.

The early scientists and primitives were both wrong. The world-wide weather observations of today have established the fact that the air over us is divided into huge air masses—continents of air drifting with the winds of earth. These air

Fierce winds and extreme cold batter the twin peaks of Mount McKinley, Alaska.

masses have vastly differing characteristics and, as they drift over our part of the world, they vary our weather and cover us with alternate umbrellas of rain, snow, or sunshine.

Although the theory that the atmosphere is divided into distinct and separate islands of air is less than 60 years old, it has already solved many of the riddles of weather phenomena. It explains cold days in May and why the southwestern air of the United States is so clear. It unravels the puzzle of the thunderstorm and the reason for fog, and it allows our weathermen to predict the weather with an average correctness of over 85%.

Basically there are only two sources of weather air. The most important one is the polar region where the great *winter air masses* are born. These are, obviously enough, formed of cold air; since cold air does not hold much moisture, the polar air masses are relatively dry. The second source lies near the equator. This is the spawning ground of the *tropical air masses* which are warm, wet, and heavily cloud-laden.

The polar air masses are built in the higher altitudes above the 40th parallel over the arctic seas or the icecapped lands near the poles. Continental polar air masses originate primarily near the desolate tundras and wastelands of Canada and Siberia. The polar air mass called *maritime polar* forms over water. Most of the snow which falls on the United States comes from the clouds generated in one of these air masses.

The tropical air masses, as the name implies, are generally created in the equatorial regions between the Tropic of Cancer and the Tropic of Capricorn. Continental tropical air masses are formed over the arid lands of the Middle East, Africa, and Australia. Occasionally one will form over Mexico. This type of air is bone-dry—so dry that it holds no further interest for us.

Maritime tropical air masses breed over the warm equatorial waters. As a consequence, these air masses absorb enormous quantities of water mist and are extremely cloudy.

In addition to these basic types, meteorologists have given names to smaller air masses because of their local importance. Those which bear mentioning are the *Arctic, Equatorial, Monsoon* and *Superior air masses*. In general these are only extreme cases of polar or tropical types. Arctic air is found on the Antarctic continent, Siberia, and occasionally Canada. It is the coldest air on the face of this earth. Equatorial and Monsoon air are found over southeast Asia and are extremely moist and warm.

Superior air is something of a mystery. It is very dry and usually exists at high altitudes. Superior air is believed to result from large-scale settling motions in the upper atmosphere. Occasionally such an air mass will overrun maritime air and come sliding down the damp slope to descend to ground level and cover the southwestern plains of the United States and Mexico. The visibility in this clear, dry air is remarkable; some Texans claim they can see over 100 miles—which is not a very great distance in the State of Texas.

Just as the nations of the world are separated by their boundaries, air masses are kept apart by barriers of their own making called *fronts*. Unlike the continents, however, air masses are usually on the move. In rare cases where geography constrains them, they may be walled-in like lakes, captured by the natural barriers of the land. An

example of this is the North Pacific air mass which nestles against the Olympic Range located in the State of Washington, held there by the westerly flow of air aloft. A similar air mass, known as the Azores High, exists along the coast of Spain. But such cases are rare. Air masses may remain in the same region for long intervals, but eventually they begin to move, and in travelling they create the changing cycle of weather. The air mass is a chameleon with an ability to assume the temperature and humidity of the surface over which it flows. If this surface is different from its origin, if it is hotter or colder or more moist or dry, the air mass will accommodate itself to the new condition, sometimes losing, sometimes gaining moisture, and changing the weather below as a consequence.

A specific illustration is perhaps the best way of explaining the weather changes resulting from the voyage of an air mass. Continental polar air will often surge through the United States from its Canadian breeding ground. At the beginning of its journey, temperatures range down to $-40°$, and the citizens of the State of Minnesota huddle against their stoves. As the air travels southeast, it absorbs heat from the land. By the time it reaches the southern states, temperatures are rarely below freezing. At this point it is shunted

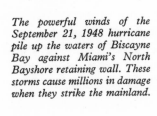

The powerful winds of the September 21, 1948 hurricane pile up the waters of Biscayne Bay against Miami's North Bayshore retaining wall. These storms cause millions in damage when they strike the mainland.

seaward over the warm Gulf Stream by the tropical maritime masses swirling north from the equator. Once over the Gulf Stream, the wandering air mass picks up both heat and moisture. In the normal course of events, driven by the westerlies, it will reach the European continent. As it encounters that cool surface, it will lose heat. Since cold air cannot hold as much moisture as hot, clouds will form and the water mist will condense into rain. Finally, the air mass will return to what it started out to be: cold, dry air.

In their surges across the fields and seas, the air masses do more than vary the weather. In a wholly automatic way they are the thermostats of earth, regulating its temperature by distributing its heat. The story of this heat distribution starts with the oceans. Water heats more slowly than land. It reflects about 60% of the solar radiation, leaving only 40% to be absorbed. Land, on the other hand, absorbs 90% and reflects only ten. Unlike the land, the oceans do not store their

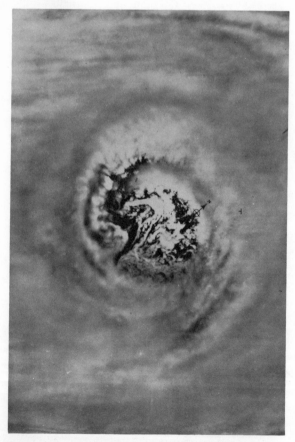

Looking down from a U-2 reconnaissance plane into the eye of Typhoon Ida in September, 1958, the counterclockwise wind pattern of the storm is clearly observable.

heat on the surface to be siphoned away by the winds; their mobile currents, however, distribute warmth to the vast ocean depths. Moreover, it takes four times as much solar heat to raise water one degree than it does to heat an equivalent amount of earth.

For these reasons the oceans have become the great moderators, acting to narrow the extremes of temperature in the air masses which journey over them. These air masses, in turn, pass on the beneficial effects of the water to the land. An excellent example of this heat-transfer process can be found along the coast of the State of California during the summer. Cool maritime air from the Pacific Ocean flows over the sun-baked California farmlands, keeping them so cool that the range in temperature between summer and winter in San Diego in Southern California is less than ten degrees.

Along the equator, tropical air masses absorb water and are heated by the seas below. This air expands, becomes lighter, and rises through the troposphere. As it reaches the higher levels, some of its heat is conducted away to the surrounding air. This leaves the rising air cooler and it can no longer retain the huge quantities of moisture which it carried aloft from the evaporating seas below. As a result, clouds form, blotting out the sun, and cooling rain falls. Thus the air masses serve to regulate the heat absorption so that the lush tropical regions are not burned by the direct rays of the sun. Another dissipation of solar energy occurs in the hurricanes created by the tropical air masses. Huge quantities of heat are transformed into the motion of the wind and waves during these storms.

In this way, the air masses air-condition the earth in the same manner as the forced air systems in houses heat and cool rooms. Heat is brought to cool areas and moisture to dry regions. The total effect creates the miraculously narrow range of temperatures which exists on our globe and allows us to live in relative comfort on most of its surface.

Weathermen follow and report the movements of air masses because this allows them to estimate the nature of weather to come. This information has become so much a part of our daily lives that we scarcely notice it, unless, of course, the prediction does not come true. To the aviator, however, weather knowledge is of more than casual

This break in the clouds was caused by seeding with dry ice. Seeding causes clouds to disperse by condensing their moisture to form rain or snow.

interest, because he must gamble his life on its accuracy.

We mentioned earlier that air masses are separated by fronts, the region where two air masses are competing for the same space. The aviator will make every effort to avoid such fronts, since they are the areas of great atmospheric turbulence and the source of most bad weather. However, there is a very considerable amount of bad weather which occurs within an individual air mass. Fogs, thunderstorms, easterly waves, and tropical cyclones are weather problems within an air mass which plague airmen and surface-dwellers alike.

Fog is the airman's most serious foe. It can be produced by cooling air masses until all of the moisture present is condensed. We ourselves create this type of fog as we breathe our lung-warmed air out into the winter cold. Another type of fog is formed in warm weather by simply adding more moisture than the air can hold. The plume of steam from the whistle of a steam locomotive is an example of such fog.

Although the pilot finds all types of fog equally objectionable, the meteorologist distinguishes fog by the manner of its creation. There are, for example, several types of cooled-air fog. *Advection fog* is formed when moist, warm air passes over cool water or cool land surfaces. This type is very common on the east coast of the United States. It

occurs when air masses warmed by the Gulf Stream pass over the Labrador current which extends its icy fingers along the coast.

Upslope fog is extremely dangerous to the unwary pilot because it usually obscures rocks. This fog occurs on mountain slopes when moist air from the sea is shunted up by mountains into the upper and colder altitudes. Such fog is really a cloud lying along the ground and is often seen rising up mountain sides during the early morning hours.

Most of us are familiar with the summer fog which forms under cloudless skies during the afternoon and evening following a warm sunny day. It is caused by radiation. The solar energy absorbed by the land during the day is radiated back into the atmosphere after the sun goes down. The loss of heat cools the surface air and precipitates its moisture as fog.

Most formations of clouds occur when air masses of different temperatures collide. Sometimes the results of these collisions are quite spectacular. Large-scale mixing of air masses often occurs very rapidly. When this happens, the atmosphere somersaults and thunderstorms are born. These storms begin to form when huge quantities of water mist are lifted into clouds which blot out the sun. Then, like the Monday-morning wash hung on the line to dry, the moisture is wrung out of them to drench the land

A hurricane-driven wave towering many feet into the air crashes at the approach to a bridge. Half the roadway (bottom of wave) has already collapsed under the ceaseless pounding.

in torrents. Static electricity is produced by the friction of the falling raindrops, the charges build up, ultimately to discharge into the ground below. This lightning causes a temporary vacuum in the atmosphere and the air, swirling in to fill the space, creates the thunderclap.

In addition to fog and thunderstorms as air-mass weather phenomena, there are two disturbances which originate in maritime tropical or equatorial air and travel in a direction opposite to that of storms in the temperate latitudes. These are called *easterly waves* and *tropical cyclones*.

An easterly wave is merely a bend in the inter-tropical front. It is oriented in a northeast-southwest line which moves irregularly westward. Along this line, thunderclouds build and showers have their maximum intensity; the wind may shift from northeast to southeast as the storm passes by.

The two types of easterly waves are mainly identified by their areas of rain shower activity. The stable wave is characterized by clear skies preceding the weather and then about 24 hours

of light-to-moderate shower activity. This type has very few thunderstorms and is quite common around tropical islands bordering the Caribbean.

The unstable easterly wave is usually an active disturbance with rainfall and thunderstorms occurring over a period of one to two days. There are usually showers on both sides of the line squall; in many cases an unstable wave is the parent of a full-fledged hurricane or typhoon. To cite an example, hurricane Carol of the 1952 season was spawned east of Miami, Florida, within an unstable easterly wave which unloaded eight inches of rainfall on the island of Puerto Rico in a 24-hour period.

Such storms may be transformed into raging tropical hurricanes by microscopic changes in the upper air-flow pattern. It is often true in nature that the difference between order and confusion is an extremely narrow containment of many complex variables. In the case of the hurricane, the difference between a sunny day and a violent storm is the consequence of only a minor shift in the atmospheric balance.

Bright fingers of lightning strike the earth during a thunderstorm.

5. Battle Lines in the Sky

THE STRIFE AND TURMOIL OF EARTHLY INHABITANTS are mirrored in the sky where the shifting air masses live with each other no more peacefully than do the man-made nations below them. In fact, a vast, world-wide meteorological war is continuously in progress as the air masses invade the territories of other air masses. These sky battles are waged along the common boundaries which, we have already mentioned, are called *fronts*. The fronts mark the interlocking of two radically differing atmospheric societies and they are responsible for most of the world's stormy weather. Like the great air masses they divide, the turbulent fronts travel over the earth from west to

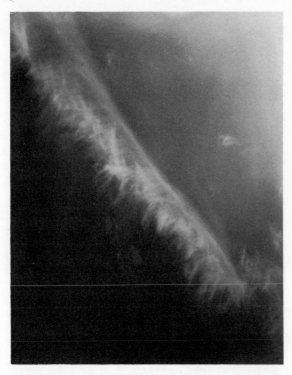

A brief veil of cirrus clouds is seen high in the stratosphere.

east to provide an ever-changing panorama of weather.

As with man-made politics, all border clashes do not provoke shooting wars, and many fronts pass over us without so much as a drop of rain or a cloud to obscure the sun. Such boundary zones are called *weak fronts* by weathermen and are caused by the meeting of air masses whose temperature and moisture content are similar. When the air masses differ radically in their temperature and moisture, the resulting front is said to be strong and the frontal passage is accompanied by violent rain, sharp wind shifts, and rapid temperature changes. Most of the rain, almost all of the vast blankets of covering clouds, and a large percentage of turbulent winds are generated in strong fronts.

Although weathermen have many names for the fronts which drift across our sky, they are usually classified according to the temperature of the air behind them. Those fronts which are followed by colder air are logically called *cold fronts*. On the other hand, *warm fronts* are followed by warm air. Since these two air-borne battle lines cause more than three-fourths of our weather, we will examine them more carefully.

A cold front develops when the leading edge of a cold-air mass meets the trailing edge of a warm-air mass. Cold air, being heavier, will under-run warm air in the same manner that a shoe can be slipped under a rug. Because of this under-cutting movement of air, the front of the cold-air mass forms a gigantic, invisible wedge of atmosphere extending back from the point of surface contact. The upward curve of this wedge constitutes the cold front and provides the battle-ground for the most violent skirmishes of the meteorological war. The cold front consists of turbid mixtures of hot and cold air, gusty winds, and vertically developed clouds which present a dark and foreboding appearance. Long lines of these "cumulo-nimbus" clouds extend throughout the length of the cold front, rising skyward like giant mountain peaks. They are characterized by an anvil-like tip which is shaped when their tops are flattened by the strong westerly winds of the upper atmosphere. Violent rain, squeezed out of the warm air as it is pushed up, drenches the earth below, while thunder and lightning form a fitting backdrop for the battle.

The cold front is usually heralded by high cirrus clouds which ride like lacy messengers well ahead of the storm. These are blown from the tops of the billowing thunderclouds which are next to follow them. Finally, the surface front arrives with its vertical clouds, heavy rainstorms, and gusty winds. These winds generally blow from the south or southwest. As the surface front passes, the winds shift radically to the northwest and the temperatures drop, often with startling suddenness. The cold-front skies clear rapidly once the surface front passes, and the damp, cool atmosphere soon has a gemlike clearness.

A warm front develops when a warm-air mass follows a cold-air mass. The light, warm air rides up above the cold, producing a soft creamlike blanket over the heavier milk of the cold-air mass. Thus the warm front also forms a wedge of cold air over the earth. But unlike the cold-front wedge, the warm-front wedge extends ahead of the surface front. It is also much flatter than that of the cold front and its weather extends over a greater area. While the average cold front has a cross-sectional width of 50 miles, the warm front is usually about 200 miles wide.

Warm-front boundaries are a zone of atmospheric battle resembling exactly those of the cold front. The moisture of the rising warm air con-

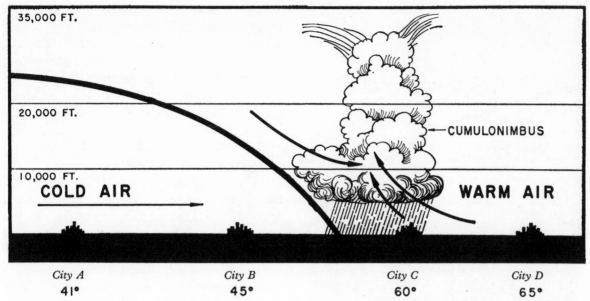

City A	City B	City C	City D
41°	45°	60°	65°

A fast moving cold front. Many of these travel over us each year with no more weather than a line of thunderstorms to mark their passage.

denses to form clouds and bring rain. However, there is a sharp difference in the form of these clouds. They lie over the land in a flat blanket which slopes down to the surface boundary. The rain falls in a monotonous drizzle which may last for days. There is very little thunder and lightning, and the winds are light instead of gusty. High cirrus clouds drift in softly ahead of the warm front and gradually thicken into a solid layer of grey clouds. As the surface front approaches, one has the feeling that one can reach up and touch the slow moving clouds. The visibility is poor; often thin fog forms in the steady rain ahead of the front. As with all frontal passages, the wind shifts, usually from easterly to southerly as the front passes. The air becomes noticeably warmer behind the front. Compared to the slashing, beachhead type of battle of the cold front, warm frontal passages have the personality of heavy slowness characteristic of a long winter battle campaign.

When accompanied by temperature changes, the sudden shifting of rain-laden winds is the surest indication of a frontal passage and of better

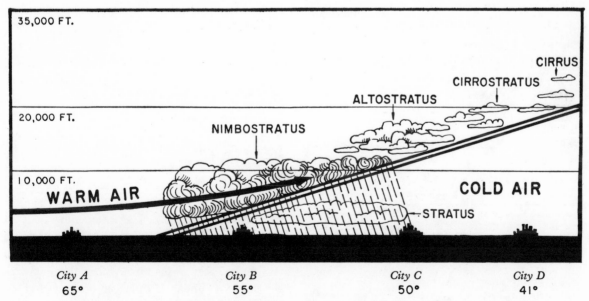

City A	City B	City C	City D
65°	55°	50°	41°

A stable warm front, showing the characteristic wide band of stratus clouds and a large area of drizzle.

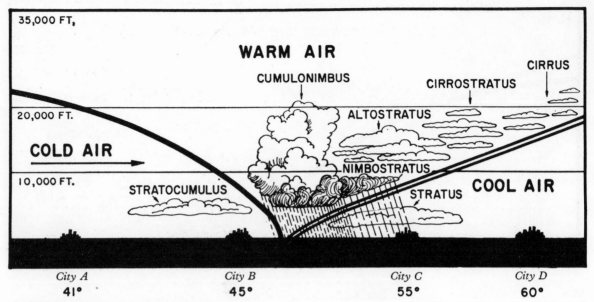

	35,000 FT,			

WARM AIR

CUMULONIMBUS   CIRROSTRATUS   CIRRUS

20,000 FT.   ALTOSTRATUS

COLD AIR   NIMBOSTRATUS

10,000 FT.   COOL AIR

STRATOCUMULUS   STRATUS

City A	City B	City C	City D
41°	45°	55°	60°

A cold front occlusion above the meeting point of the two surface fronts. Normally, a cold front occlusion moves rapidly, and the region contains the most intense weather battles of the aerial war.

weather to come. Weathermen, observing these facts on their recording instruments, earn an easy reputation for reliable forecasting while the local weather is still bad. We can forgive this easy victory, however, when we realize that these opportunities are rare and that for the most part they must study endlessly the areas hundreds of miles away in order to predict the local weather.

The passage of the giant storm fronts becomes a continuous cycle as the air masses travel their great atmospheric routes. They weave the local sky into a pattern of ceaseless change, providing variety and diversity to make the air alternately grey and blue, sunny and rainswept, dappled with tufted cirrus, or darkly coated by low stratus. The result is distribution. Water is brought to the arid land and heat is delivered to the cold places of the sphere. Just as the ships carry their cargo

from one nation to another over the world's waterways, so do the weather fronts transport the riches of the atmosphere over the earth. Areas neglected by the treasure-laden fronts are for the most part shunned by living things. Some lie as tranquil and barren deserts under the pitiless sun, while others are coated by eternal frost.

In the Northern Hemisphere, fronts move from west to east at an average speed of 15 miles per hour, but they do not always travel at the same rate. The reason for this difference in velocity lies in the variation in the air pressure between the air masses. Some contain relatively dense air which rises to great heights over the earth; such air masses exert high pressure on the surface below them and result in what weathermen call *high-pressure zones*. Dips and valleys also occur in the atmosphere, and the air masses which contain them are said to possess *low-pressure zones*. High-pressure air tends to flow to a low-pressure area much as water can be sucked from a "high-pressure" glass into a "low-pressure" mouth through a tube. For this reason high-pressure air following a low-pressure air mass will be sucked to the low pressure and will gradually overtake the low-pressure air mass. The intervening body of air, caught between these two opposing pressure systems, will slowly be squeezed skyward until its fore and rear fronts meet. When this happens, the point of contact is called an *occlusion* and the new line of battle is termed an *occluded front*.

COLD   WARM

COOL

City A	City B	City C	City D
41°	45°	55°	60°

The cold front occlusion shown above, as it would appear on the daily weather map.

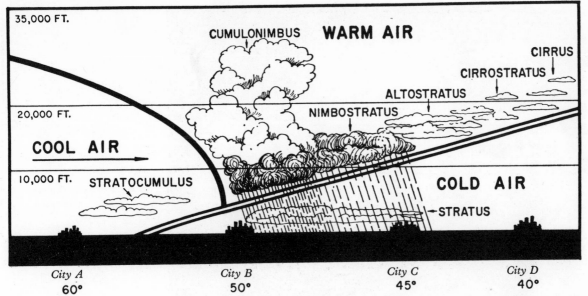

35,000 FT.

CUMULONIMBUS **WARM AIR**

CIRRUS

CIRROSTRATUS

ALTOSTRATUS

NIMBOSTRATUS

20,000 FT.

COOL AIR

10,000 FT. STRATOCUMULUS

COLD AIR

STRATUS

City A
60°

City B
50°

City C
45°

City D
40°

A warm front occlusion, showing the cool air rising over the cold front. Warm or cool air, being lighter, always rises above cold air when two such air masses collide. Warm front occlusions move slowly and may bring rain lasting several days.

The blue waters of the Pacific Ocean are often the spawning ground of these occluded fronts. As the warm and cold fronts sweep inland like ocean waves to cross the western shoreline of the United States, they are delayed by the high coastal mountain ridges. Occasionally this delay permits later fronts to catch up and engage the straggler, producing occlusions and occluded fronts at the points of contact. Other occluded fronts are formed over the prairie plains of the mid-western United States when the polar continental air mass sends icy fingers stabbing southward. Such bulges in the polar front are called *waves*. As these waves deepen, their sides draw closer together. Eventually contact occurs between the leading and following edges—each a true front in its own right—and an occluded front is born. The early stages of this process, before the fronts meet, produces the weather phenomenon known as a *wave cyclone*.

Three types of air are involved in the occluded front. The central section just below the occlusion is covered by a blanket of warm air. The region just before the front is cool; the air following the front is definitely cold. The conversion of a wave cyclone into an occluded front takes place when the pressure drops in the warm middle sector, causing the two fronts on either side to approach and make contact like the claws of a lobster. When this takes place, the warm air is gripped between the cool- and cold-air masses and squeezed aloft.

In a practical sense this means that occluded fronts cause cold surface weather since the warm air is lifted away from the earth's surface.

The exact characteristics of occluded fronts depend upon whether the coldest air lies ahead of, or behind, the occlusion. When the coldest air lies ahead of the surface front, the system is known as a warm-front type occlusion. Another type of occluded front occurs when the coldest air is behind the surface front. As before, the warm air is pushed aloft, but the front remaining on the surface is now the cold front which has nudged its way under the cool air.

From the standpoint of a ground-dweller, the passage of an occluded front does not appear significantly worse than the passage of a strong cold front. Both types of weather are equally bad. However, the appearance of an occluded front on

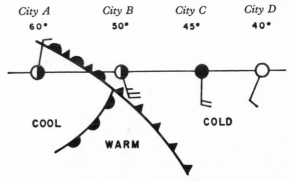

City A 60°   City B 50°   City C 45°   City D 40°

COOL   COLD   WARM

The warm front occlusion diagrammed above, as it would appear on the daily weather map.

37

Cumulo-nimbus clouds often form at the sides of mountains when the winds blow upslope, bringing warmth and moisture from the valleys below.

his weather map is a matter of the greatest concern to an aviator. One of the most important features in his flight planning is the avoidance of that area near the occlusion where the warm and cold fronts meet, for here the meteorological combat is fought in its most violent form. Giant thunderstorms, extreme turbulence, slashing rain, and assaulting lightning greet the unhappy aviator who has the misfortune to blunder into these destructive areas. Of the two types of occluded fronts, the cold-front occlusion is the more violent since the energy of the warm-front type is spread over a larger area. If either one lies in his path, however, the wise pilot plots a detour to avoid both types of ambush.

So far in this chapter we have discussed the influence of the three major frontal types upon our weather. In general the passage of these fronts, coupled with the individual characteristics of the air masses themselves, account for most weather. However, some unusual aspects of the frontal systems affect our everyday life and warrant a closer look.

Most people who live in warm coastal climates have experienced the squall or, more exactly, the pre-frontal squall. Very few people have encountered the squall's violent relative, the tornado, which we shall discuss fully in a later chapter. The pre-frontal line squall often occurs together with a cold front when the winds aloft are stronger than those at the surface. When this happens, the frontal weather is whipped ahead of the surface front like foam from the crests of waves in a high wind. Such squalls arise suddenly and, although of brief duration, can be extremely violent, smashing roofs, uprooting trees, and capsizing sailing craft. Only its localized radius of action and short duration prevent the squall from becoming a major enemy of man.

The sinister, majestic thunderstorm is the siege gun of the weather war. Within its dark and turbulent depths exist the last remnants of the primeval struggles which convulsed the young earth during its formative millennia. The black, writhing pillar cloud and the tufted ramparts and battlements which surround it have awed man throughout the ages. Even the ancient Greeks, sophisticated in art and philosophy, credited the thunderstorm with godlike powers. They explained its lightning as the wrath of their god Zeus, who was said to hurl the bolts from his own hand. Early primitive peoples gave the thunderstorm a place of respect second only to that accorded to the mighty sun. The English language is filled with descriptive phrases which epitomize the storm as the ultimate in speed and might, such as *quick as lightning, loud as thunder,* and *a bolt from the blue.* These and many other expressions

Cumulus and stratus clouds mix together to create a confused and darkened sky. These formations often occur in weather fronts.

show how deeply the thunderstorm has impressed itself upon man's consciousness, and with good reason. Although often more catastrophic, weather is never more dramatic than when it appears as the titan thunderstorm.

The anvil-topped thunderhead, called *cumulonimbus* by weathermen, can be created by many conditions warring in the atmosphere. The most familiar of these is the cold-air mass thunderstorm which occurs with great frequency, particularly in the interior of the United States, during the spring and summer months. During these seasons cold-air masses creep over the land surfaces which have been baking under the sun. The earth acts as a giant stove and heats the lower layers of atmosphere, and the warming air absorbs moisture as a sponge. This hot air then rises, expanding and boiling and spiralling up into the colder regions above.

The expanding air quickly loses its heat and commences a process which resembles that of the Monday-morning wash as it goes through the wringer. The higher the air rises, the less its pressure becomes, the more it expands, and the more it is cooled. Finally, the water mist, which had been carried aloft with the warm air, begins to condense. The resulting fair-weather cumulus clouds dapple the afternoon sky on many a warm afternoon.

Very few of these plumed cumulus clouds grow into full-fledged thunderstorms. In appearance they are fluffy and round, with a flat bottom; generally they are all at exactly the same height. To an aviator flying beneath them, they appear like a batch of rising yeast rolls, sitting on an invisible pan, ready to be popped into the oven. As the plane flies under them, it is bumped and jolted by the rising air currents which feed them. Glider pilots and soaring birds fully appreciate this phenomenon and wisely fly below such clouds to use the up-currents which rise beneath them.

By watching these clouds, we can sometimes see a thunderstorm born before our eyes. If the moisture content of the air is high, if the day is hot, and if the upper air is unusually cool, the cumulus clouds continue to build until they tower high in the sky. The interior of the clouds changes from fluffy white to an ominous black. Water droplets form and are shunted up by the up-sweeping air. Some of these travel higher and higher until they rise above the freezing level. At this point they harden into hailstones. The hailstones become larger—often as big as golf balls—when they are joined by water droplets from below. Finally, when the rising air can no longer support its burden, rain and hail begin to fall. At this point, the thunderstorm is said to have reached its mature stage.

39

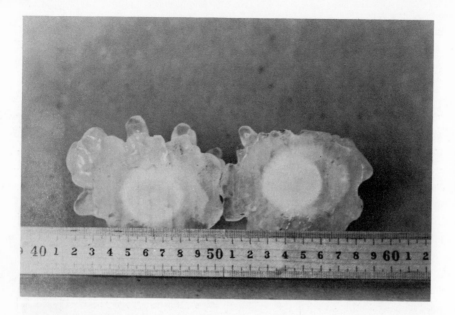

Huge hailstones such as these often fall to earth in severe storms and, like snowballs rolling down hill, they increase in size as they travel. Large stones are produced when ice crystals are driven high into the clouds by violent updrafts.

As the rain and hail mix and boil in the cloud, they produce static electricity in much the same manner as a comb produces static charges when rubbed over a cat's back. Under the abrasive action of the atmosphere, the electrical charges grow and combine until the thunderhead is a gigantic storehouse of electrical power. The central portion of the cloud becomes negatively charged; the upper and lower layers acquire a positive charge. When the difference in electrical potential grows to about 50,000,000 volts, flashes of lightning rend the sky. Air in the path of the discharge is pushed aside and a near-vacuum is instantaneously created. The stricken atmosphere hastens to heal its scar and the air rushing into the void creates the noise we know as thunder.

As the storm grows older, the thunderhead may eventually form an anvil top. This will occur when the top of the cloud reaches a height at which it is caught by the high-velocity winds aloft. At this point the roll cloud at the bottom will be most pronounced and the thunderstorm will have achieved its most classic form. Generally, the flow of air in the thunderstorm is upward from the rear and forward and down at the front. If you are near a thunderstorm and feel a blast of cool air, you can be confident that the storm is coming your way.

The dissipating stage begins as the down-currents spread throughout the storm. Since the upper air is cooler, these down-currents chill the cloud. Finally there are no up-currents in the storm, and the cloud itself begins to die. If we watch a thunderstorm through its final stages, we will notice that the cloud becomes much thinner and tends to flatten out or *stratify*, in the words of professional weathermen. The life of a thunderstorm is amazingly short, and the cycle from beginning, through roaring storm with thunder, lightning, and precipitation to complete dissipation rarely takes more than a few hours. Some cumulo-nimbus clouds attain the awesome height of 60,000 feet while others rise no more than 30,000 feet.

The modern aviator has a healthy respect for the destructive thunderstorm. If at all possible, he will attempt to fly around it; if he cannot do this, he may turn around or seek to penetrate the storm at a low altitude. When he does go through a thunderstorm, he will be prepared for a rough ride. He will brighten his cockpit lights so that blinding flashes of lightning will not leave him momentarily sightless, unable to see the instruments. He will caution his crew to strap themselves in tightly to prepare for the turbulence. He will also watch carefully for the light-greenish color which is characteristic of clouds containing hail.

Hailstones are a real hazard to flying, although the smaller ones are of no particular significance. However, in bad thunderstorms where the up-currents have been violent enough to keep the small hail pellets above the freezing level until they have become large—sometimes larger than baseballs—hailstones are very dangerous. These larger stones are weather shrapnel which not only destroy aircraft but sweep across the earth's surface with a destructive flail which demolishes crops, dents cars, breaks windows, and in general menaces life and limb. Fortunately, the severity of such bombardments is short-lived, and damage is usually confined to small areas.

On the nuisance side, one of the most aggravating weather situations is that which occurs when we are afflicted by continuous rain. Life in general becomes exasperating when the skies are covered with leaden rain clouds for days on end. Small children must stay indoors, shopping is difficult, the ground is soft and muddy, and only the taxi driver faces each oncoming wet day with assurance. Such periods almost always occur when an overhead front stagnates and ceases to move. Such weather conditions are called *stationary fronts*. They often occur when two air masses align themselves (over the United States, for example), with high-pressure areas to both east and west. Occasionally, cold air from Canada and moist air from the south, bringing up thousands of tons of moist air from the Gulf of Mexico, meet in stationary fronts. These conditions produce a perfect rain factory and are often the cause of great floods over the midwestern United States. Intense fronts on the move also deposit huge quantities of rain, but the precipitation is spread over a wide area. When fronts cease to move and the entire war takes place in one area, the results may be disastrous.

The rocky gorges and tree-crested slopes of the Rocky Mountains are often the scenes of another type of stationary front. The moist, warm air of the Pacific Ocean emerges here with the sharply contrasting dry, cold continental air from the Canadian plains. The turbulence of the front is further intensified by the air shunted up by the mountain range. When a cold-air mass lies over Canada, temperature differences across this front can be as much as 80° or 90°, and a battle royal ensues over the stationary front. These conditions help to explain why there are no major industrial cities in the Rocky Mountains.

An unusual weather phenomenon involving a nonexistent front occurs near the equator. Over this hot spot lies a band of weather commonly called the inter-tropical zone of convergence or equatorial front. Actually this zone is not a front

Various cloud forms march across the sky, some close to the earth, some high in the stratosphere. Others, like the awesome cumulo-nimbus, have low bases but extremely high tops. These generally produce the most violent weather.

Middle clouds such as alto-cumulus often precede the great weather fronts as they move across the American continent.

at all. By definition, a front is the meeting place of two contrasting air masses. By contrast, the inter-tropical front lies entirely within the tropical air mass and in reality is produced by large-scale vertical air movements. The heat of the sun beating down on the equatorial atmosphere acts as a giant elevator to lift the moisture-laden air. Violent weather results from the meeting of the up-flowing warm air and the cold currents of the stratosphere. This battle area may extend from the surface to great heights, and it contains some of the most turbulent currents known to our atmosphere. The equatorial convergence zone fluctuates in position and intensity each day, following the sun in its annual trip north and south of the equator. The incredible energy of the tropical heat evaporates millions of tons of water, to be condensed into massive tropical thunderheads which tower 40,000 and 50,000 feet above the coral seas. When the saturation limit is reached, torrential rain lashes down to shower some tropical islands with more than 30 inches in a single day. This amount is considered a good rainfall for an entire year in most parts of the world.

In this chapter we have outlined the great airborne global conflicts which produce stormy weather. The knowledge of air masses and their meteorological battle lines which we call fronts is far from complete. Indeed, 50 years ago the term *front* did not exist. However, for the first time in the history of our earth we are no longer subject to the surprises and whims of the ever-changing, eternal cycle of weather. Although our present ability to forecast is limited to a few days ahead at best, our techniques will advance as more information becomes available. After reviewing the marvellous strides of the past half-century, who can tell where we will be in the next? This much is certain: each passing year will increase our independence from the elements of our planetary environment.

A flood caused by heavy spring rains brings a torrent which overruns the towns around the river.

6. The Imperfect Balance

ON JANUARY 29, 1953, A SMALL LOW-PRESSURE area developed in a cold-air mass about 200 miles south of Iceland. The birth of the resulting storm went practically unrecorded except by the few ships which happened to be passing through those cold and seldom-travelled seas. To the sailors, who were familiar with the storm-lashed North Atlantic waters, another storm was not remarkable.

Due to a combination of somewhat unusual circumstances, however, this storm was unique.

At the same time that the low-pressure area was deepening, a high-pressure belt of warm air, stretching from Africa to Iceland, began moving east to meet it. The result was the most violent European storm since the year 1703.

The North Sea, which separates England from Norway and Denmark, is formed like a gigantic funnel. Almost 300 miles wide between Scotland and Norway, it narrows to not more than 20 miles at the English Channel. The small cyclone, now grown lusty, was pushed rapidly past Ireland to

This ocean liner sank on January 31, 1953, after an encounter with 115-mile-per-hour winds in a violent ocean storm.

the mouth of the funnel by the flow of high-pressure air from behind, gaining in intensity all the way.

As bad luck would have it, the storm developed during a period of unusually high tides. By January 31 it was full-grown, with winds which roared with terrific force at speeds up to 115 miles per hour. On the crest of the high tides, the waves became mountainous. On the morning of January 31, the storm suddenly caught up with the *Princess Victoria*, a 2,700-ton ferry placidly nosing its way across the North Channel to Ireland. Within moments, the ramp doors of this vessel were smashed and the engine room flooded, leaving the little ship helpless. It was quickly blown across the Channel by the raging winds. Five miles from the Irish coast, the boats were lowered. Many were smashed and most of the remainder capsized. As a result, 132 of the passengers and crew lost their lives; only 14 were saved.

The storm traced a path of devastation across the northern tip of Scotland down into the North Sea funnel. Portions of the east coast of England around Norfolk have been reclaimed from the sea and are protected by huge dikes. More than half of Holland lies below the level of the high tides and is kept dry only by similar sea walls. As the storm struck the dikes in full fury, they were first cracked and then punctured by huge, gaping holes. The north winds blew bitterly cold and the waters which drove over the land were flecked with chunks of ice.

By February 2, the storm was dying and reduced to fitful gusts. By now, the damage was estimated at hundreds of millions and each new tide brought new floods to the country of the Netherlands. Two thousand people were killed and thousands more left homeless. The work of rescue and reclamation began immediately and required a major national effort. This was the

High water marks are recorded on the walls of an old church on the west coast of England.

44

Battling the waters of a fierce flood, workmen struggle to rebuild a sandbag barrier and divert the water from residential areas. The midwestern United States are often plagued with these disasters.

worst storm in 350 years and three years were needed to repair all the damage done.

Cold fronts such as the one we have just described often sweep across the North Atlantic during the winter months. The icy winds and high waves which they generate are so frequent as to be the general rule rather than the exception. Fortunately, however, the world weather conditions seldom combine to build cyclones as violent as the great storm which slashed across Europe in 1953. However, the oddity is not that these terrible, destructive storms occur, but that we are not afflicted with more of them.

Indeed, it is necessary to probe only superficially into our universe to find far greater atmospheric disturbances. The fantastic storms which daily sweep across the surface of the sun are 100,000 miles in diameter, 10,000 miles high, and millions of degrees hot. By comparison, the worst of our earthly cyclones is scarcely a ripple in the pool of cosmic energy. Astronomers have found that even the atmosphere of the sun must be considered placid when its turbulence is compared with that of many other bodies found in the heavens.

We cannot dismiss this comparison by saying that the earth and other planets are different from the burning stars because, although this is true, the earth's atmosphere and materials contain the same inherent energy. Furthermore, we are constantly flayed by the fierce rays of the sun and other cosmic bodies. It is only because of the hair-thin balance existing in the atmosphere that

we are saved from being vaporized by this tremendous bombardment which beats down upon us with a continuous force equal to 250,000,000,000 horsepower. Life is permitted to exist only by the swirling atmosphere which dissipates and apportions this radiated energy. The great cold-front storms are one medium through which the circulating atmosphere reduces the enormous quantities of trapped solar heat.

The tremendous force of a hurricane is demonstrated by this piece of timber that was driven through the trunk of a palm tree.

45

As a result of these processes, the heat released to the earth's surface is a mere fraction of the total radiation which comes our way. The vast remaining bulk of solar energy is kept in balance by the miraculous, orderly mechanism we call atmosphere, and that atmosphere provides the means whereby the millions of tons of radiation forces are matched and neutralized by other equally gigantic forces. The resulting state of neutrality allows us to live in our world.

In the face of this huge massing of energy, man can be compared to an ant living near a giant dam. Occasionally droplets splash over and the ant is convinced that the heavens are descending upon him. But this temporary inconvenience is nothing when measured against the cataclysm which would obliterate the ant's world if the dam were to burst.

It is these tiny droplets of weather which are inflicted upon our world. Because they have become a part of our daily experience, we are much more aware of them than we are of the delicate balance which keeps the enormous forces of the universe from destroying us. But the balance is ever precarious. Occasionally it suffers a minor upset, and for a brief moment we catch a glimpse of the titanic energy around us. When this happens, the mightiest forces created by man, even the hydrogen bomb, are dwarfed by comparison. The swirling clouds of the smallest hurricane contain the energy of thousands of hydrogen bombs. In the face of such phenomena we are reminded again of the narrow and miraculous margin by which we are protected from extinction.

The balanced energy in the earth's atmosphere demonstrates its strength in truly incredible ways once it becomes unsettled. This fact is often illustrated in startling and terrorizing fashion to the modern airman, as indicated in the following true experience.

One winter day during the war year of 1944 a United States Air Force pilot was flying a heavily loaded cargo plane over The Hump, that rugged mountainous strip of land which contains the Himalaya Mountains and separates India from China. He was "on instruments" and flying through thick, freezing clouds which caused heavy layers of clear ice to build on his wings. The minimum safe altitude for his route was 15,000 feet. Somewhere in the misty void ahead of him was a mountain over 13,000 feet high, but his plane was unable to maintain even that much altitude. In fact, he was now flying at 9,000 feet, just barely able to nurse the plane along at minimum safe flying speed with the maximum power setting he could use.

The pilot was in real difficulty. It looked as though he had the choice of crashing head-on into the side of the mountain or bailing out with his crew into the wild, barren Himalaya steppes below. The latter alternative was almost certain to result in death by exposure, but at least it

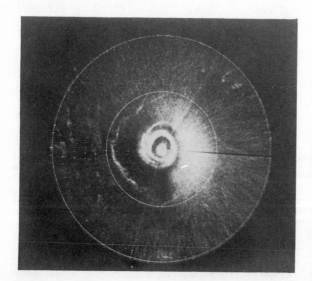 

(Left) The rainy eye wall of a hurricane is viewed by radar just before cloud seeding. (Right) Shortly thereafter the forward wall has begun to disappear as silver iodide crystals cause liquid water droplets to convert to snow crystals.

A typical evening fog in London blankets all but a brightly lighted bus. Note the people at lower left.

offered a bare chance of survival. He was just about to hit the warning button to notify the crew to bail out when an amazing thing occurred. The 50,000-pound aircraft began gaining altitude at the rate of 2,000 feet per minute as though some giant hand was lifting it up!

At 16,000 feet, the pilot nosed the plane over, but he gained 2,000 feet more before he was able to stop the sudden climb. At slightly over 18,000 feet, he was finally able to level off the plane and settle back with a sigh of relief.

Was this some miracle unique in modern flying? Not exactly.

Every aviator has encountered such strong vertical gusts in flight. They are the result of local air currents which develop in the mobile air masses similar to the way eddies and swirls appear in a running brook. Generally these gusts impart only a slight bump to aircraft in flight and their vertical speed is only a few feet per minute, but they serve as a constant reminder to the flier that the

atmospheric balance is seldom perfect. Our pilot had the good fortune to blunder into the giant upgusts of a growing thunderstorm when he needed a lift. He was lucky, indeed, for the odds were equally good that he would hit strong downgusts which might have shattered his aircraft and crew against the rocky gorges below.

The titanic forces of the atmosphere produce other, quieter phenomena which also bedevil us, and in some cases their formation is assisted by man himself. This is particularly true with some types of fog. Formerly a minor nuisance except to navigating ships and aircraft, in recent years fog has become a major problem in many areas. Its feathery mists and cloying dampness are common weather phenomena found almost everywhere in the world. Actually, fog is another name for clouds which lie along the surface of the earth. As an illustration, suppose we find a cloud layer 2,000 feet above the surface of a valley joining a nearby mountain. A weather station in the valley would

Atomic "fallout" is a new and deadly pollution. Scientific workers chart the radioactivity after an atomic burst.

report a cloud layer 2,000 feet high. A station on the side of the mountain above 2,000 feet will report fog.

During recent years a very curious and steady increase has taken place in the incidence of fog over the world's industrial areas. For a long time scientists were puzzled by this development until they noticed the striking corollary between the increase in fog and the growth of manufacturing industry. Studies showed that, as new factories were built, fog crept over the surrounding towns with increasing frequency. This fog was different from the pure mists which develop naturally when moisture-laden air is cooled. It was often yellow and contained toxic gases which made people sick and sometimes even killed them. They called this new killer *smog*.

As new factories are constructed, their stacks belch additional loads of chemicals and combustion products into the already overburdened atmosphere. Much of this air-borne debris is too heavy to be carried by the winds, and it falls as grime to smear city streets. Some of the lighter particles and the waste gases, however, remain air-borne, to be dissipated slowly by the winds. This pollution is not serious until water-laden air

combines with it in an unholy alliance to form smog. Once a rare and temporary irritant, the mixture of fog and industrial pollution now hangs over many of our cities to befoul the air and kill living things to such an extent that it has become a major problem.

In December, 1952, the city of London was blanketted by one of its famous pea-soup fogs. Cleaning winds had died until there was no movement in the air. Transportation and communications ground almost to a halt, but the city continued to pump the vast accumulation of its smokestacks into the stagnant atmosphere. Meanwhile, the death rate rose appallingly by more than 900 a day, more than at any other time except during the great cholera epidemic of 1834. Within four days 4,000 people died of the polluted air. The mortality rate of new-born infants almost doubled and there were many deaths among older people, mainly from bronchitis and pneumonia. All this from one fog!

Continuing their investigation of smog, weathermen found nearly twice as many foggy days in Prague, Czechoslovakia, after 1880 as there were between 1800 and 1880. The industrial Ruhr region of Germany receives more drizzle than surrounding areas, although both are subject to the same weather pattern. Investigation into these situations produced the startling fact that local weather conditions were directly geared to the pollution of the atmosphere by industrial plants.

Further study showed that atmospheric dust was a distinct factor in the formation of the water droplets which compose fog and clouds. The dust acts as a condensation nucleus which allows the minute water particles in the air to cling to it and form larger drops. If moisture droplets are to reach a size at which they may be seen in the form of rain and clouds, these condensation nuclei are necessary, and the presence of myriads of such nuclei greatly aids the formation of rain, fog, and drizzle.

On days when there is a breeze which dissipates air pollution, the situation is not critical. The dust nuclei are distributed throughout the surrounding atmosphere and any fog which forms is quickly blown away. The worst effects are felt during periods of unusual calm with a temperature inversion which allows the smoke and haze to hang low over the earth. This condition was responsible for the killing fog of London, and a similar in-

WORLD WEATHER EXTREMES
TEMPERATURE (degrees F)

LOWEST	BRITAIN	−17	Braemar, Aberdeen	Feb. 11, 1895
	AUSTRALIA	−8	Charlotte Pass, New South Wales	Aug. 22, 1947
	THE UNITED STATES	−78	Fort Yukon, Alaska	Jan. 14, 1934
		−70	Rogers Pass, Montana	Jan. 20, 1954
	CANADA	−81	Snag, Yukon Territory	Feb. 3, 1947
	GREENLAND	−87	Icecap	Jan. 9, 1954
	THE WORLD	−126.9	Vostok, Antarctica	Aug. 24, 1960
HIGHEST	BRITAIN	100	Greenwich Observatory	Aug. 9, 1911
(in shade)	AUSTRALIA	127.5	Cloncurry, Queensland	July 10, 1913
	THE UNITED STATES	134	Death Valley, Calif.	Jan. 16, 1889
	THE WORLD	136	Azizia, Libya	Sept. 13, 1922

PRECIPITATION (inches)

HEAVY RAINFALLS	In 15 minutes	7.80	Plumb Point, Jamaica	May 12, 1916
	In 42 minutes	12.00	Holt, Missouri	June 22, 1947
	In 2¾ hours	22.00	D'Hanis, Texas	May 31, 1953
	In 18 hours	38.00	Kadena, Okinawa	Sept. 8, 1956
	In 24 hours	45.99	Baguio, Philippines	July 14-15, 1911
	In 2 days	65.79	Funkiko, Formosa	July 19-20, 1913
	In 7 days	131.15	Cherrapunji, India	June 24-30, 1931
	In 31 days	366.14	Cherrapunji, India	July, 1861
	In 12 months	1,041.78	Cherrapunji, India	Aug. 1860-July 1861
HEAVY SNOWFALLS	In 24 hours	76	Silver Lake, Colo.	Apr. 14-15, 1921
		62	Thompson Pass, Alaska	Dec. 29, 1955
	In one storm	175	Thompson Pass, Alaska	Dec. 26-31, 1955
		152	Norden, Calif.	Mar. 30-Apr. 4, 1958
	In one month	390	Tamarack, Calif.	January, 1911
	In one season	1,000	Rainier Park, Wash.	1955-56
		884	Tamarack, Calif.	1906-07

ATMOSPHERIC PRESSURE (sea level . . . inches)

HIGHEST	31.75	Irkutsk, Siberia	Jan. 14, 1893
	31.53	Medicine Hat, Alberta	Jan. 24, 1897
	31.40	Helena, Montana	Jan. 9, 1962
LOWEST	25.90	Typhoon "Ida," 750 mi. east of Luzon, Philippines	Sept. 24, 1958
	26.18	S. S. "Sapoerea," 460 mi. east of Luzon, Philippines	Aug. 18, 1927
	26.35	Craig, Long Key, Florida	Sept. 2, 1935

WIND VELOCITY (miles per hour)

HIGHEST	231	Mt. Washington, N.H.	Apr. 12, 1934
	183	Blue Hill Obs., Milton, Mass.	Sept. 21, 1938

version often plagues the dwellers of Los Angeles. Smog conditions are such that a few factories must shut down on calm days to avoid serious pollution.

During recent years, several methods have been devised to rid our skies of this aerial rubbish. The precipitator perfected in the United States by Dr. Frederick Cottrell is a good example. His system utilizes a screen which is placed over the factory smokestack. This screen carries an electric current which electrifies the dust particles as they pass through it. Plates which have an opposite charge pull the dust particles out of the air.

This and other devices have been very successful, but there is still a great deal to be done before industrial cities will have air which is free from pollution. Those who live in large cities breathe in vast amounts of dust carried by the atmosphere each day—over 50,000 particles per breath. Many areas have practically no plant life; pollution is the reason. The effect of such conditions on our health, cleaning bills, and the condition of our buildings is incredible. Today we are on the threshold of cleaning up our air, just as we were beginning to purify the earth by the installation of proper drainage and adequate sewers only a single century ago. It is to be hoped that the next 100 years will show as great an improvement in the atmosphere around us.

In this chapter we have discussed the miraculous balance of forces which produces our weather and permits us to live. Nowhere is this balance more delicate than in the razor-thin temperature band which exists near the surface of our planet, for it is here that the atmosphere acts as a gigantic and marvellously efficient air conditioner to stabilize our daily temperature. The deathly cold of outer space, located but a celestial hair's-breadth above our heads, is 400° below zero. At this level, all molecular action ceases. From this low point, the universal temperature ranges up to millions of degrees. The temperature of the sun, at a depth where the atmospheric pressure equals that of the earth, is over 900,000°, while the heart of the sun is estimated to boil at 100,000,000°. As an illustration of the magnitude of such temperatures, it is worth noting that diamonds vaporize at 8,000°. By contrast, the temperature on earth has never been recorded as less than 127° below zero, nor does it ever rise higher than 136° on the Fahrenheit scale. This indicates a spread of a mere 230°, as compared to the 1,000,000° swing which we know exists in the universe.

If the earth were to swing inward a trifle on its sun-surrounding orbit, our oceans and rivers would boil away. The solid crust itself would sear and cracks would open in the earth, exploding inner fire; the handful of humans who burrowed below to escape the unchecked radiation pouring through a previously protecting atmosphere would soon perish.

Move the earth away from the sun, edge it nearer the next outermost planet, Mars, and killing cold would descend to mantle our sphere. The growing polar caps would merge with the swiftly freezing waters of the oceans; the consequent redistribution of weight could be sufficient to shift the earth's axis and, in a single cosmic

The smoke pots located at various levels on this tower demonstrate that the wind can blow from several directions at the same time. However, this is an unusual phenomenon.

instant, violently destroy all living things. Perhaps this would not occur. Survivors might descend to the tropics, there to postpone temporarily the inevitable freezing end to life.

But man is an egotistical bit of fragile jelly, and he is not so much concerned with the fact that his surrounding temperature band is narrow in a celestial sense as he is with the fact that it is so broad in a human sense. Although outer space is infinitely colder, 94° below zero is bitterly cold to our human bodies. Below −60°, man is unable to face the elements with so much as a square inch of skin uncovered, and water freezes instantly with a loud cracking noise. The unpleasant world-record low of −126.9° Fahrenheit was recorded at Vostok in the Antarctic.

The wastelands of the arid Near East, south of the Mediterranean, hold the unenviable record for heat. The hottest day ever recorded was inflicted upon the residents of Azizia, a little town near Tripoli in North Africa when the temperature rose to 136°. Perhaps this helps to explain why the Moors invaded Europe more than 16 centuries ago; it is possible that they were seeking a cooler climate. The United States holds the runner-up record; one blazing day the mercury hit 134° in aptly named Death Valley.

Endless statistics can be found to demonstrate

The Beaufort wind scale

Beaufort Scale or Number	miles per hour		Result on land and sea.
0	0–1	Calm	Smoke rises vertically; sea, mirror calm.
1	2–3	Light Air	Direction shown by smoke drift but not by wind vane; small wavelets.
2	4–7	Light Breeze	Wind felt on face; leaves rustle; wind vanes move; short waves.
3	8–12	Gentle Breeze	Leaves and twigs in motion; extends a flag; crests begin to break.
4	13–18	Moderate Breeze	Raises dust and paper; moves small branches; white horses on the sea waves.
5	19–24	Fresh Breeze	Small trees in leaf begin to move.
6	25–31	Strong Breeze	Telephone wires whistle; large branches begin to move.
7	32–38	High Wind	Whole trees in motion.
8	39–46	Gale	Twigs break off.
9	47–54	Strong Gale	Slight structural damage; signs blow down.
10	55–63	Whole Gale	Trees uprooted; considerable structural damage.
11	64–72	Storm	Damage widespread (seldom occurs except on Gulf coast and East coast).
12	73 & over	Hurricane	Hits Gulf coast and moves northeastward to coastal states; waves higher than 45 feet.

the giant strength of the forces which create our weather. Some are hard to unearth because of the violent extremes which they attempt to measure. For example, devices which are designed to record the strength of the wind have the unhappy habit of blowing away in the face of really violent gusts, along with the buildings on which they are located. The highest winds are found in tornadoes, and reliable estimates have placed the winds at greater than 500 miles per hour in some of these storms.

Tropical hurricanes produce the most extreme weather conditions at sea. Often, the interaction of wind, storm, and sea is so violent that the horizon disappears and the sailor's world becomes an inseparable mixture of swirling air and water. During February, 1953, a churning wall of water as high as a 15-storey office building battered the U.S.S. *Ramapo* in the North Pacific. This wave was observed by the crew to extend up to the mountainous height of 119 feet. The enormous power of this storm can be appreciated when it is compared with the violent explosion on the volcanic island of Krakatoa in 1883 which killed thousands of people, blanketted the world with dust for weeks, and obliterated the island from the face of the earth. It caused a tidal wave of approximately the same height!

The storm observed by the crew of the *Ramapo* is so extreme that no provision exists even to catalogue it. The height of waves at sea is measured by the Beaufort Scale. Beaufort numbers range from zero when the winds are calm and the sea is like glass to Beaufort 12 when the winds are above hurricane force and the waves over 40 feet high. Beaufort 6, for example, describes weather conditions where the winds range between 25 and 31 miles per hour and the waves run about 12 feet. On this scale, the *Ramapo* wave would have been a hypothetical Beaufort 36!

An awesome tropical hurricane as it unleashes its violence.

7. The Twisting Winds

The Sailing Directions for the Northwest and North Coasts of Norway is a matter-of-fact, businesslike document published to acquaint mariners with the special problems associated with ocean voyages in these tricky, storm-tossed waters. It does not deal with the superstitions of the ancient Norsemen who sailed the seas in their fragile craft, nor does it contain any unnecessary speculations about the mysteries of the little-travelled seaways it describes. However, in one passage, the reader has the feeling that he is reading a page straight from the pen of Edgar Allan Poe. This is the portion which describes the maelstrom which runs between the islands of Masken and Lofotodden:

"... as the strength of the tide increases the sea becomes heavier and the currents more irregular, forming extensive whirlpools. During such periods no vessel should enter the Moskenstraumen. These whirlpools are cavities in the form of an inverted bell, wide and rounded at the mouth and narrower toward the bottom; they are largest when first formed and are carried along with the current, diminishing gradually until they disappear; before the extinction of one, two or three more will appear like so many pits in the sea . . . Fishermen affirm that if they are aware of their approach to a whirlpool and have time to throw an oar or any other bulky body into it the water must rush suddenly in on all sides and fill up the cavity."

Just as these whirlpools form in the eddies and currents of the earth's waters, so they flash into being in the sea of air above. Many of them run short but dizzy races over the midwestern plains of America as whirlwinds or "dust devils" on hot summer afternoons. Generally these rise suddenly from beneath clear skies, creating swirls of dust and sharp, gusty winds. They move swiftly across the land in erratic paths as though they were nature's buffoons performing a whimsical dance to break the monotony of a hot day; seldom do they produce any more serious damage than to upset outdoor furniture or shatter an occasional window.

However, there is another type of twister which has the same sort of relationship to the dust devil as a hungry tiger bears to a playful kitten. This is the most fearful and mysterious of all nature's weather phenomena: the tornado.

The tornado is not mysterious because it is a rare phenomenon which occurs only in remote sectors of the globe. Quite the contrary; during the first six months of 1962, the United States alone was struck by 280 tornadoes causing the death of more than 500 persons and doing damage estimated at many millions of dollars. But the fearful proportions of these storms and the suddenness with which they strike the farms and cities of the "tornado belt" have kept man from gaining any real knowledge about them, despite all the progress of modern science. Man can therefore resort only to the ancient device of escape when he hears its roar and sees the delicate-looking, tenuous tube of the tornado approaching him. He can only run, huddle quivering in a cavelike storm shelter, or lie flat against the earth if he is to avoid destruction.

As storms go, the tornado is one of the smallest. Generally, the terrible black mouth which sweeps over the land is a circle whose diameter is between 50 and 1,000 feet. Seldom does the

The terrible, broad funnel of a mature tornado.

destructive area approach a mile in width, and the average path is about 13 miles long. However, some twisters have travelled 200 to 300 miles before dissipating, and often there are large "skip distances" when the angry cylinder rises up from the earth and leaves the ground below untouched.

The terrible damage done by these storms in the United States is illustrated by the fact that during a period of 22 years Illinois lost 814 lives; Georgia, 433 lives; Texas, 441 lives; and Alabama, 611 lives. On June 9, 1953, a tornado swept through Worcester County, Massachusetts, wrecking some 2,500 homes and killing 83 persons.

The exact nature of the weather elements which must combine to permit the birth of a tornado is one of the most perplexing mysteries of modern weather science. It is known that they usually develop as a result of the meeting of two air masses. In the tornado belt, the warm moist air from the Gulf of Mexico drifts slowly northeast. At the same time, cool, dry air masses from the plains of Canada dip south in undulating waves; tornadoes form within the meeting zone between these air envelopes having different temperatures.

As the moist Gulf air is heated from below by the sun-drenched farmlands of Texas, Oklahoma, and Kansas, it rises and the moisture condenses

The early stages of a tornado.

into billowing cumulus clouds which mushroom up like smoke from an open fire. When the heated air flows aloft, it produces local areas of low pressure in the region of the meeting zone, and this causes both hot and cool air to rush into the gap below. Since the warm air and the cool-air mass from the north are flowing in different directions, a shearing or rotating force develops. The resulting flow pattern is similar to that produced when we pull the drain plug from our bath; a whirlpool of air develops around a low-pressure focus. However, instead of water rushing out through a drain pipe, the central core of hot air rises up thousands of feet into the sky at speeds of over 100 miles an hour.

At first, when we pull out the bath plug, only the surface water appears to rotate but, as the whirlpool gains momentum, the focus deepens until it extends all the way down to the drain pipe. The same thing happens during the formation of a tornado, allowing the spinning cylinder to touch the surface of the earth when a certain critical balance in the pressure relationship of the winds is reached.

The tornado cone descends from under a heavy, black, very turbulent cumulo-nimbus cloud which is accompanied by violent gusty winds. Milton Tabor happened to be under such a cloud in Topeka, Kansas, on the afternoon of March 23, 1913, just as a tornado was forming. He graphically described what he saw: "The tornado cloud formed near where we were enjoying a picnic and whirled furiously, high in the air straight over our heads. We looked up into what appeared to be an enormous hollow cylinder, bright inside with lightning flashes but black as blackest night all around. The noise was like 10,000,000 bees,

plus a roar that beggars description." This storm later did terrible damage in Omaha, Nebraska.

The United States Weather Bureau has recently established a Tornado and Severe Storm Research Project in order to study this phenomenon. Since the violence and suddenness of a tornado's growth are so great that they prevent first-hand study, the weathermen have planted instruments along the usual pathways of twisters in the states of Kansas and Oklahoma. By means of these instruments they hope to measure the internal pressure, wind speed, and amount of rain inside a tornado.

The damage inflicted by a tornado exhibits much of the freakish tendency of other violent weather phenomena. There have been cases where houses have been demolished by storms and the furniture carried away, only to be found later without a scratch. Straws have been driven deep into boards. Strong buildings have been destroyed while flimsy structures next to them came through the storm undamaged. In one instance a herd of cattle was picked up by a tornado and lifted high in the air until the cows appeared like great birds. Chickens are sometimes stripped of their feathers but otherwise unharmed.

In May, 1931, the *Empire Builder*, a train which travels between Chicago and Seattle, was speeding over the United States' western flatlands when the engine-driver sighted a tornado which looked as though it would cross the steel tracks ahead. Since his train was one of the most modern on the line, with passenger cars built entirely of steel, he was not particularly worried. Nevertheless, he slowed his speed somewhat to evade the storm. However, the twister veered suddenly and passed directly over the passenger cars. These weighed almost 65 tons each, but five of them were wrenched off the rails and wrecked by the awful power of the storm.

Under the impact of a tornado many buildings appear to explode. This is because of the vacuum created within the vortex of the storm. Since the air inside enclosed structures is at atmospheric pressure, this outer vacuum produces a powerful bursting pressure which destroys wooden and masonry walls as though they were paper. Generally, strong mortar buildings suffer the least damage. Multi-storey structures invariably lose their roofs and may suffer severe damage to their upper stories while the lower levels remain intact. Often tornadoes can be escaped easily by driving or even running at right angles to the storm path.

During the 1953 season there were almost three times as many tornadoes in the United States as there are during normal years. Many laymen and some scientific observers believe that these were due, at least in some measure, to the large number of atomic bomb blasts carried out for test development purposes. Official statements from United States government scientists have repeatedly reassured the American people that there is little if any basis for this belief. They point to the fact that atomic bomb blasts are tame compared with the fury of a tornado, and that the development of these storms does not appear to have any correlation with the atomic bursts.

On the other hand, some eminent physicists mention the fact that only a few ounces of silver iodide drifted into a cloud are sufficient to trigger thousands of tons of rainfall. They insist that in a like manner, the A-bombs may trigger the violent, explosive tornado. Following bomb blasts, they say, the air is filled with radioactive dust particles. Physically, this dust is very similar to that which is used in cloud seeding. If the weather conditions are just right, they believe that these charged dust particles may be the cause of our current crop of twisters.

In support of their theory, they cite the case of the Eastman Kodak Company located in Rochester, New York. Ever since the first of the atomic blasts detonated in the United States, Eastman has had trouble with its sensitive photographic film, despite the fact that the firm is located almost 3,000 miles from the testing ground. In fact, officials of the company are now warned whenever bomb tests are to about be conducted so that they can take steps to safeguard their valuable films. Some scientists believe that if atomic dust can cause its characteristic milk-white coating to form on the surface of film 3,000 miles away, then it is also possible that the same dust can be the cause of tornadoes over the Midwest and even the eastern United States.

Modern scientists are all willing to admit that the weather equation is a hair-thin balance of many complex variables. Some very minor variations are known to result in major weather changes; therefore, while there is no positive proof that atomic bombs have any general effect upon weather, the possibility cannot be discounted. The final answer will be known only when we have a better understanding of weather phenomena.

Many pictures of tornadoes have been taken. Some of these show the storm as a straight cylinder from top to bottom; others are larger at the

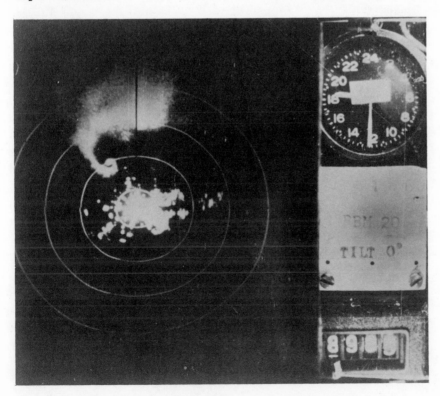

Radar picture of storm clouds as seen from a weather plane. Weather reconnaissance aircraft are flown to obtain warning of approaching storms.

bottom than at the top; and some have an hourglass figure. Generally, the funnel seems to bend and sway back and forth as the storm travels over the ground.

On January 3, 1949, a tornado developed near Warren, Arkansas. Mr. B. P. Hughes of the United States Weather Bureau had the opportunity of flying along the path of this tempest shortly after it had dissipated. He found that the storm had passed over the southern edge of Warren, a town of about 7,500 people. Near the focus of the path, nothing was left standing. The ground appeared to have been burnished by a gigantic power buffer and reflected light like a strip of waxed floor which had been recently polished. The destruction was complete out to a width of about 300 feet in each direction from the middle of the tornado's path. There was an area of decreasing damage for another three or four hundred feet on either side. He also noted that the path of destruction contained several "skip-distance tracts" which exhibited no damage at all. The storm had travelled its entire course in a northeasterly direction with little deviation from a straight line. The local area was very wet indicating that a large amount of rain had fallen during the storm.

Although tornadoes have been reported at all hours of the day, most of them occur in the late afternoon and early evening. In Kansas, 75% have commenced between noon and 8 P.M.

A number of people have been trapped inside a tornado and lived to tell of the experience, but few were trained weathermen. Captain Roy S. Hall, United States Army, Retired, who lives in the little town of McKinney, Texas, has made the study of weather his hobby. He not only survived the terrors of a tornado but also wrote a fascinating account of his experiences.

Captain Hall was sitting placidly in his back yard talking with his wife on the warm afternoon of May 3, 1948. He had noticed several small thunderstorms muttering and grumbling in the southwest but had given them little attention. His wife remarked that the wind was blowing from the south at about 25 miles per hour and exerting a steady pressure against the leaves of the nearby trees. A short time later Captain Hall was surprised to hear a loud clap of thunder. Looking to the west he noticed that a huge, very black cloud obscured the entire horizon. Below this cumulo-nimbus was a feathery roll cloud charac-

teristic of those which precede thunderstorms. Behind the roll cloud he could catch glimpses of a solid curtain of dark green rain. The air appeared very humid and the temperature was about 85°. In graphic terms, Captain Hall in the magazine *Weatherwise* described what followed:

"The squall, now about two miles away, was coming directly toward us, and the scud cloud, stretched across its front between 400 and 500 feet above the earth, was revolving as if it were being pushed in reverse along the ground. Behind the scud cloud, dark green rain was falling in a solid opaque wall. The south wind was veering. In a matter of a few seconds it had changed, and was blowing, undiminished, from the southeast toward the cloud. Lightning, the most fearful I have ever seen, and wide as a house, flashed with some regularity between the scud cloud and the ground. In the comparative stillness following the terrific thunder crashes I could hear a sustained hollow roaring, like a distant freight train."

Captain Hall and his family sought shelter in their house. When the low roll cloud moved overhead, the visibility decreased as with the coming of night. Hailstones larger than tennis balls began falling around the house, striking the roof and the yard with a loud clatter. From the sound, he could tell that some of them were tearing through the ceiling. Lightning was now striking all around the house. Captain Hall discovered with horror that the west wall had slipped inward about six inches at the ceiling and was vibrating under the force of the wind. Between flashes of lightning it was coal-black outside, but Captain Hall was able to catch brief glimpses of the next-door house and the surrounding yard. He noticed that the shrubs and trees were blown almost flat, and that the air was filled with debris. His eardrums were buffeted by a roar like that of a fast freight train booming through a long tunnel. His story continues:

"And then very suddenly, when I was in the middle of the room, there was no noise of any kind. It had ceased exactly as if hands had been placed over my ears, cutting off all sound, except for the extraordinary hard pulse beats in my ears and head, a sensation I had never experienced before in my life. But I could still feel the house tremble and shake under the impact of the wind. A little confused, I started

The delicate and distant tube of this tornado is seen just before it struck Conway, Arkansas, on April 11, 1965, causing damage so severe that President Johnson declared the state a disaster area.

to look out the north door, when I saw it was growing lighter in the room. The light, though, was so unnatural in appearance that I held the thought for a moment that the house was on fire. The illumination had a peculiar bluish tinge, but I could see plainly. I saw the window curtains lying flat against the ceiling, and saw loose papers and magazines packed in a big wad over the front door. Others were circling about the room, some on the floor and others off it. I came out of my bewilderment enough to make a break for the back of the house.

"But I never made it. There came a tremendous jar, the floor slid viciously under my feet, and I was almost thrown down. My hat,

which I had not removed, was yanked off my head, and all around, objects flashed upward. I sensed that the roof of the house was gone.

"As I gained footing another jarring wham caught me, and I found myself on my back in the fireplace, and the west wall of the room had collapsed right down on top of me. The "whams" were just that. Instead of being blown inward with a rending crash of timbers, as one would expect of a cyclonic wind, the side of the room came in as if driven by one mighty blow of a gigantic sledge hammer. One moment the wall stood. The next it had been demolished. The destruction had been so instantaneous that I retained no memory of its progress. I was

57

standing, and then I was down, ten feet away. What happened between, I failed to grasp or to sense.

"By a quirk of fate I was not seriously injured, and as soon as I had my senses about me I clawed up through the wreckage, and crawled around and through the hole where the east door had been. I could tell by the bluish-white light that the roof and ceiling of this room were gone also. I almost ran over my four-year-old daughter, who was coming to see about me. Grabbing her up, I was instantly thrown down on my side by a quick side-shift of the floor. I placed her face down, and leaned above her as a protection against flying debris and falling walls.

"I knew the house had been lifted from its foundation, and feared it was being carried through the air. Sitting, facing southward, I saw the wall of the room bulge outward and go down. I saw it go, and felt the shock, but still there was no sound. Somehow I could not collect my senses enough to crawl to the small, stout back room, six feet away, and sat waiting for another of those pile-driver blasts to sweep the rest of the house away.

"After a moment or so of this, I became aware that I could see the next house, standing unharmed 100 feet to the south. Beyond I could see others, apparently intact. But above all, I felt a vast relief when I saw that we were still on the ground. The house had been jammed back against trees on the east and south and had stopped, partly off its foundation.

"The period of relief I experienced, however, was a very short one. Sixty feet south of our house something had billowed from above, and stood motionless, save for a slow up-and-down pulsation. It presented a curved face, the concave part toward me, with a bottom rim that was almost level, and was moving neither toward nor away from our house. I was too dumbfounded for a second even to try to fathom its nature, and then it burst upon my befuddled brain with a paralyzing shock. It was the lower end of a tornado funnel. I was looking at its inside, and we were, at the moment, within the tornado itself!

"The bottom of the rim was about 20 feet off the ground, and had doubtless destroyed our house a few minutes before as it passed. The

A tornado reaches downwards towards the earth, moving swiftly and haphazardly along its destructive path.

interior of the funnel was hollow, the rim appearing not over ten feet in thickness and, owing possibly to the light within the funnel, perfectly opaque. Its inside was so slick and even that it resembled the interior of a glazed standpipe. The rim had another motion which I was, for a moment, too dazzled to grasp. Presently I did. The whole thing was rotating, shooting past from right to left with incredible velocity.

"I lay back on my left elbow, to afford the baby better protection, and looked up. In that upward glance my stricken eyes beheld something few have ever seen before and lived to tell about. I was looking far up the interior of a great tornado funnel! It extended upward for over 1,000 feet, and was swaying gently and bending slowly toward the southeast. Down at the bottom, judging from the circle in front of me, the funnel was about 150 yards across. Higher up it was even larger, and seemed to be partly filled with a bright cloud, which shimmered like a fluorescent light. This brilliant cloud was in the middle of the funnel, not touching the sides, as I recall having seen the walls extending on up outside the cloud.

"Up there, too, where I could observe both the front and back of the funnel, the terrific whirling could be plainly seen. As the upper portion of the huge pipe swayed over, another phenomenon took place. It looked as if the whole column were composed of rings or layers, and when a higher ring moved on toward the southeast, the ring immediately below slipped over to get back under it. This rippling motion continued on down toward the lower tip.

"If there was any debris in the wall of the funnel, it was whirling so fast that I could not see it. And if there was a vacuum inside the funnel, as is commonly believed, I was not aware of it. I do not recall having any difficulty in breathing, nor did I see any debris rushing up under the rim of the tornado, as there surely would have been if there were such a vacuum. I am positive that the shell of the twister was not composed of wreckage, dirt or other debris. Air, it must have been, thrown out into a hollow tube by centrifugal force. But if this is true, why was there no vacuum, and why was the wall opaque?

"When the wavelike motion reached the lower tip, the far edge of the funnel was forced downward and jerked toward the southeast. This edge, in passing, touched the roof of the next house and flicked the building away like a flash of light. Where, an instant before, had stood a recently constructed home, now

remained one small room with no roof. The house, as a whole, did not resist the tornado for the fractional part of a second. When the funnel touched it, the building dissolved, the various parts shooting off to the left like sparks from an emery wheel.

"During pistol practice in the Army, when the light was favorable, I have seen bullets from a .45 pistol flash from a gun to target. The bullets have a known velocity of 825 feet a second. The white planks from the house moved at a speed equal to, if not greater than, that of the bullets, which would establish the velocity of the tornado's rotation close to 600 miles per hour. This, I believe, is conservative. My own conviction is that the funnel was spinning faster than the speed of sound, accounting, in some way beyond my knowledge for the total lack of noise within it.

"The very instant the rim of the funnel passed beyond the wreck of the house, long vaporous-appearing streamers, pale blue in color, extended out and upward toward the southeast from each corner of the remaining room. They appeared to be about 20 feet long and 6 inches wide, and after hanging perfectly stationary for a long moment, were suddenly gone.

"The peculiar bluish light was now fading,

The damage done by hurricanes varies greatly, depending upon their violence and the amount of warning which people have of their approach.

1

and was gone abruptly. Instantly it was again dark as night. With the darkness my hearing began to come back. I could hear the excited voices of my family in the small back room, six feet away, and the crunching jars of heavy objects falling around the house. The tornado had passed. The rear edge was doubtless high off the ground and went over without doing any damage. Quickly, real daylight commenced to spread in the wake of the storm, and how good it did look! And how astonishing! I had come to believe, those few long minutes, that the tornado had struck in the night time. It was now about 3:06 P.M."

Although Captain Hall's house was wrecked, fortunately none of his family was seriously injured. The storm passed on through the southern part of McKinney, Texas, and many people were killed and injured by it.

The most singular and awe-inspiring weather phenomenon to be found at sea is the volatile union of sea and sky known as the waterspout. This fascinating and often violent outburst of nature is a close kin to its landlocked relative, the tornado.

There are some important differences between the land variety of twister and those which inhabit the oceans. Tornadoes are bred and develop along the frontal zones between warm- and cold-air masses, while waterspouts form under a wide variety of ocean weather conditions. Sometimes they develop beneath sparkling sunlight without a cloud in the sky, but more often they are observed under the cumulus clouds of a frontal squall line. Tornadoes last longer and are more violent than waterspouts; furthermore, they travel faster and are somewhat larger.

Waterspouts rarely last for more than an hour and many of them complete their life cycle in less than five minutes. Although the tornado always rotates with a counterclockwise motion, the waterspout may revolve in either direction. The tube may be only a few feet in diameter or as much as 100 yards at its narrowest part. It may rise many thousand feet into the upper air or only a few feet, like the dust whirls which develop over the midwestern plains of America.

In the average case, the waterspout begins as a downward-projecting bulge from a cumulus cloud. This cloud projection lengthens seaward and at the same time the surface of the water below is disturbed by an intense, boiling eddy. The middle of this eddy lifts as though pushed from below, and the surface water is blown up in a misty spray. This spray forms the lower part of the tube which reaches up to unite with the cloud projection above. In the meantime, the air between the surface and the cloud layer has begun to whirl and condense its moisture. As the tube becomes a single vertical cylinder, the waterspout reaches its greatest intensity. By this time the waterspout cloud is dark, almost black, and the force of the wind has reached violent proportions; at this stage, a loud roaring sound accompanies the storm. Observers who have seen many well-developed twisters at sea emphatically declare that the formation of this giant of nature is invariably fearful and foreboding.

Waterspouts form in all the oceans and in many lakes. Some tornadoes become waterspouts when they pass over lakes and rivers, and often they form in chains out of elongated clouds. The sailor can never be sure when he will see a waterspout, for they develop during all months of the year. They occur most frequently from May to September.

Many observers have reported strange and unusual waterspouts. One of these had a huge bulge in the upper middle which, according to an observer, made the tube resemble the neck of an ostrich which had just swallowed a grapefruit. Another sea twister had a very complicated, twisting tube which doubled back upon itself in a large loop. At the instant the coils made contact with each other, the waterspout collapsed completely and disappeared.

The tubes of some waterspouts are made of a solid, glistening wall of water; others are composed of fine spray. Modern ships have penetrated this latter type of storm and have found that winds are only moderate and that the only noticeable effect was a thin mistiness which covered the ship as it went through. Other storms have wrought terrible damage. On August 19, 1895, a gigantic waterspout developed in Vineyard Sound, Massachussetts. This storm formed out of the base of a huge cumulus cloud and was at least 145 feet across at its narrowest part; the mammoth tube extended up over half a mile. The fact that sea water is carried aloft into the mothering cloud by such spouts was definitely shown when, hours later, salty rain containing a

The funnel of this huge Adriatic waterspout extends to the base of the clouds about 2,000 feet above the sea. The cylinder is 200 feet wide and consists of a solid water wall surrounding an open middle.

few small fish fell on Martha's Vineyard. As an aftermath of such storms, ships have been deluged not only with rain and hail, but in northern waters, with chunks of ice six inches in diameter.

Waterspouts sometimes form with two tubes, one inside the other. There are indications that water is often pulled up through the middle of the tube by the relative vacuum which exists inside the storm. The mouth of the spout generally rests upon a shelf of foam which may be several feet high and many feet in diameter. Surrounding this shelf is a cloud of spray which extends aloft for considerable distances in a strong waterspout; this spray sometimes inflicts considerable damage on nearby ships.

Modern seamen do not fear the waterspout as they did in ancient times. Due to the relatively slow speed of these sea twisters, they can be circumnavigated with ease by power-driven vessels.

There have been some rather unique theories advanced for destroying these storms, among the most unusual of which is the use of artillery fire.

According to those who believe in this method, a direct hit by the shell from a large gun would collapse a waterspout, on the theory that, once such a projectile had punctured the tube, the internal vacuum would be destroyed and the funnel would disintegrate. So far, the theory has never been tested and most modern weathermen do not believe that a momentary puncture of the tube would produce the desired effect.

The complete understanding of waterspouts and tornadoes remains one of nature's most intriguing mysteries. Weathermen know that they are the product of unstable weather conditions, but the exact mechanism which must exist to produce them is hidden behind the suddenness and fury of their development. However, modern man has found the rewards of understanding to be magnificent indeed. Because of his inquiring mind, he is no longer one of many jungle animals in mortal terror of the stronger beasts. He will continue his search for understanding of the tornado, knowing that it too will some day fade into the limbo of the once-feared.

Hurricane clouds seen from a plane at 20,000 feet.

8. The Hurricane

THE HAUNTED DAYS OF EARLY BRUTE MAN WERE filled with many terrors which developed out of vagaries in the natural world. As a youth he became aware of the thunder and lightning that flamed across his senses and unleashed sudden death. The great polar icecaps ground slowly towards the equator in their mysterious periodic swing, and he learned of cold and bitter, implacable weather storms.

Since no mortal means of protection from these phenomena were available to him, he created immortal ones in the form of holy images which he worshipped and to which he offered sacrificial gifts. And as the winds lashed him and the deadly chill settled in his caves, his courage was kept alive only by faith in these gods.

One such deity was known as Huracan, meaning "god of all evil." It was created by a tribe of aborigines called the Tainos who established an extensive culture in the Greater Antilles and Bahama Islands. Although the Tainos are now extinct and their civilization is long buried beneath tropical growth, their word with its suggestion of dread lingers on.

Half a world away, in the Pacific Ocean where the same great storm is called the *typhoon*, the fear is just as real. On the great coral islands which dot the Pacific storm belt, panic-stricken natives offer up sacrifices—formerly human sacrifices—so that they may be spared from destruction. During World War II there were indications that the invading Japanese soldiers succumbed to the local tradition. These soldiers, capable of suicidal charges in battle, were no braver than the conquered natives in the face of the storm. They likewise made offerings to the dreaded typhoon god.

There are no earthly furies capable of comparison with the hurricane. Life exists only because these storms are relatively rare and because their force is spread and dissipated over many thousands of square miles. Scientists, who have estimated the hurricane's violence, say that it would take the continuous explosion of 1,000 atomic bombs a minute to equal the energy output of a moderate storm. Thus, man's mightiest weapon is a mere firecracker when compared with this gigantic sky-borne artillery.

The damage wrought by these storms is truly incredible. In 1900 the edge of a hurricane struck Galveston, Texas. That brief encounter killed 6,000 people, and devastated the city. This havoc, the greatest-ever in the United States, pales into insignificance when compared with a typhoon which roared through the Bay of Bengal on October 7, 1737. When the winds subsided, 300,000 persons were dead. Entire areas were stripped of human life. Others were completely devastated, every structure smashed flat against the pulpy ground. Over 20,000 boats and vessels were sunk. This, the worst natural disaster of all time, almost equalled the number of American servicemen killed in World War II.

The sensations produced by the force of hurricane winds are similar to those which would be felt by a man strapped to the nose of a modern airliner in full flight. Average winds of 150 miles per hour are common; gusts of 250 have been registered in some storms. Winds of this titanic power surge the sea's surface into giant tidal waves which engulf ports and the cities that lie beyond them. With casual flicks, such waves beach ocean-going liners and roll cars down debris-strewn streets in grim imitation of a monstrous bowling alley. Entire houses are often wrenched from their foundations and hurtled against those of other houses; cities are sometimes completely destroyed. Rain accompanies the wind, but on an unbelievable scale and like no other rain known to this earth. The world's record rainfall of 46 inches, at Baguio in the Philippine Islands, occurred during a typhoon. Enough water fell during a 24-hour period to cover the entire island to a depth of over three feet.

In the face of such incredible forces, it is not remarkable that the ancient dread and awe of the hurricane persists. However, gradually we have not only learned to understand the forces which create such storms, but can now send our investigating agents into the very heart of the storm itself.

In order to understand the mechanism of the hurricane, let us explore its source regions. Hurricanes are most common in the Atlantic Ocean and the Gulf of Mexico. Similar storms originate in the band of the Pacific Ocean near Formosa and the Philippines. The only difference between the Pacific typhoon and the Atlantic hurricane is one of terminology. Great arguments have taken place between sailors and airmen as to which of the two oceans spawns the greater storms; so far the decision has gone to the side

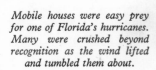

Mobile houses were easy prey for one of Florida's hurricanes. Many were crushed beyond recognition as the wind lifted and tumbled them about.

which argued the loudest. The violence of the hurricane is so awesome and extensive that measurements of its intensity are of necessity not entirely accurate. Hurricanes and typhoons always form in the hot, humid atmosphere of the inter-tropical front. This front is not really a front at all but is born within the tropical air mass as a result of the intense heat-pumping action of the sun's energy which causes the warm, wet air to rise and create clouds.

During the summer months, the inter-tropical front moves north, following the sun and undulating snakelike over the softly swelling equatorial seas. It forms a huge globe-circling belt of weather characterized by shifting, gusty winds, sudden showers, and cumulus-type clouds which swell frequently into cumulo-nimbus rising to towering heights. Because of its restless weaving from north to south, nodes and valleys form in the inter-tropical front, and these sometimes extend north far beyond the limits of the front itself. Such indentations are known as easterly waves because they move from the east, and their development brings intense showers and violent winds. The resulting instability may produce a tropical disturbance which the weathermen will begin to plot on their charts and follow carefully.

If the variables in the weather equation fall into propitious balance, and if the disturbance is far enough north so that the motion of the earth momentarily enables the winds to twist, a counter-clockwise circulation develops and a hurricane is born. The new storm soon breaks away from the mothering inter-tropical front and begins to wind

up with terrible intensity in much the same way that a tornado develops, except that it covers a much wider area.

The hurricane builds from hour to hour. Like a gigantic wheel rolling down a precipice, it gains momentum from itself, fed and nurtured by its own movement. The winds blow counterclockwise, beating the tropical seas with terrible force. Waves of 100 feet rise and follow each other in close cadence. The boiling surface of the water takes on the texture of a scorching-hot bubble bath with the spray extending several hundred feet up. Near the middle of the storm, the seas are blown flat so that their surface becomes a solid sheet of foam. Heavy clouds lie 300 or 400 feet over the ravaged water, pouring torrents of rain back into the sea.

The central vortex becomes a dead, eerie calm. Often there are no clouds overhead and the sun gleams through with an unnatural brightness. The seas are choppy and confused. Occasionally, the eye of the vortex will be filled with birds circling desperately in an attempt to escape the fury. Ships caught in the storm will often seek to ride it out within the protecting funnel of the eye. The birds land on the ships and cling desperately to the rigging, grateful for a brief respite.

Violent vertical air currents surge in the counter-clockwise swirl of the hurricane. Near the edge of the storm, these beat down against the surface. At the eye they rocket upwards, lifting millions of tons of warm air into the upper troposphere. So violent is this skyward rush that the sea surface below is actually raised up in the same manner

A hurricane-hunting plane searches for storms high over the Atlantic Ocean. The large bubble beneath the fuselage in front of the engines contains the radar.

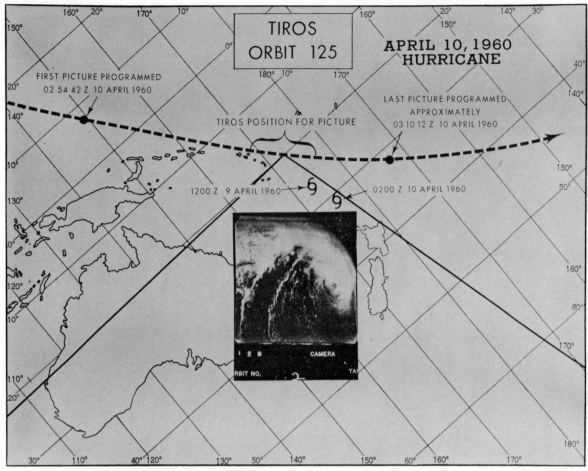

The first picture of a hurricane taken by satellite.

as water sucked up through a straw. The agitated sea, seeking to compensate for this mountain of water, convulses and sends giant tidal waves outward. Millions of tons of sea water are torn from the parent body and ascend with the air torrent at the eye. Later this mass will be returned to the surface as torrential rain during each day in the life of the storm.

Not many years ago weathermen believed that lightning and thunder accompanied hurricanes. But recent investigations have shown that there is remarkably little electrical disturbance in well-developed storms, although the reason for this remains a mystery. Definite records exist, however, of tornadoes created within hurricane storm areas. During the night of October 4, 1933, a large tropical storm of considerable intensity passed just south of Miami, Florida. In the same period, tornadoes passed through Miami, Fort Lauderdale, and Hollywood Beach. In these cases, the tornadoes did more damage than the hurricane which created them.

The development pattern of a hurricane has been studied in recent years by scientists using the wizardry of radar. Upon the blue-white electronic scope, the cloud patterns roll outward like scrolls of silver. The tenuous bright lines denoting the air flow can be traced from the weatherman's warm room at the comfortable distance of several hundred miles. But even with these safeguards, the hurricane is awesome and dreadful. Its movement and growth are plainly visible as the observer watches. In the space of a few hours the focus develops from a dark smudge to a clearly defined circle. The brilliant white area of rain clouds and turbulence enlarges with each sweep of the radar, and the course and speed of the storm are easily estimated. The trained weatherman is fascinated by the scope as he studies the mighty torrents of wind and rain, knowing that there is no greater display of the terrible fury of nature.

Nordhoff and Hall in their book *Hurricane* caught the essence of the storm when they wrote:

65

A wall of water three storeys high hurdled the banks of a river in Putnam, Connecticut, crashing down on one of the main streets. This flood was caused by two storms which developed simultaneously near the equator and moved northward together.

"The nakedness of a hurricane's truth is not revealed at once. You think you are seeing it within an hour after the wind comes, but your experience of the pitiless majesty of nakedness is enlarged from moment to moment. . . "

Although the use of radar has enabled the weatherman to locate a hurricane and track it on the move, he is still unable to predict the precise future path of the storm. At best he can only make a guess based on his knowledge of previous storms. Many efforts have been made to predict the hurricane track from accumulated data obtained from other storms. All have failed; the hurricane follows no statistical law. The terror of the skies veers and wheels as unpredictably as does its baby brother, the tornado. Its path can be almost any length or direction. The great hurricane of September, 1853, was born near the coast of Africa, and travelled almost to the eastern seaboard of the United States. Off Cape Hatteras it curved northeastward and when last plotted was heading in the direction of Greenland, travelling a destructive path of more than 5,000 miles! Contrasted to this demon, the violent storm of October, 1952, was insignificant. The October storm flared up just south of Cuba and died near the Bahamas, a distance totalling but a few hundred miles. The 1853 storm raged for weeks; the 1952 storm had a short but turbulent life of only five days.

Voluminous statistics have been compiled on the size and strength of hurricanes. So far they have yielded no statistical constants. Like the three bears, there are little hurricanes, medium-sized hurricanes, and big hurricanes. Many storms sweep over half an ocean; others are localized in small areas. Generally speaking, the small storms are likely to be more intense since the pressure drop between the eye of the storm and the outermost fringe is more abrupt. This steeper pressure drop or pressure gradient causes more violent winds.

One of the most remarkable things about science is that it gives us tools that we can sometimes use to control phenomena which science itself cannot fully explain. The fact that we do not really understand the electric flow we call electricity does not prevent us from piping it through wires, lighting our lights and driving our motors. Our knowledge of nuclear physics is far from complete, yet miracles and horror, too, have been wrought from that partial knowledge. And so it is with hurricanes. Although our understanding of the great storms is extremely limited, we have nonetheless established some very useful working principles.

The hurricane wages aerial warfare against a community as devastating as the bombing raids of World War II. Like the bomber strike, the best action short of stopping the storm (a trick

In the foreground two people can be seen waiting on a roof for a rescue boat to take them to safety after flood waters inundated their homes.

we have yet to learn) is sounding the alert. Given enough time, there is much that can be done. We can lash our outdoor belongings to the ground, shutter our windows, and, above all, get ourselves and those we love into hurricane shelters. The story of how man has succeeded in the Gargantuan task of hurricane protection is one of the least publicized and most thrilling tales of our times.

The story of organizing the hurricane alert began at the end of World War II. During the conflict radar emerged from the laboratories and became standard equipment on aircraft. Searching for deadly German U-boats, American and British radar operators noted that their instruments would often indicate a target which, when investigated, turned out to be a weather storm. They reported this fact to headquarters and went back to their monotonous search. When the war was over and planes and personnel were free from their former missions, the Joint Hurricane Warning Service was set up. The United States Air Force and Navy, and the United States Weather Bureau closed ranks in order to reduce the death toll and damage caused by the recurring hurricanes. Their reconnaissance planes probe the turbulent storms, and the United States Weather Bureau studies the resulting data to forecast the storm path and alert the unsuspecting communities involved. The combined efforts of the Joint Hurricane Warning Service have pro-

duced spectacular results and have provided one of the most valuable peacetime aids rendered to a civilian population by the military. The saving in human life alone is indicated by the fact that during the period from 1926 to 1930 there were 161 deaths in the United States for each $10,000,000 worth of property damage. Today, thanks to those who sound the hurricane alert, the death rate has fallen to about two deaths for the same amount of property damage.

A pilot once described flying as "hours of boredom occasionally interrupted by moments of stark terror." The experience of riding through a hurricane in a weather-reconnaissance plane fits nicely into this definition—except that there is no boredom. Weather-reconnaissance flying is one of the most tense and hazardous operations in a generally tense and hazardous occupation. Fortunately the crewmen on such flights are so busy that they do not have time to become really frightened until the worst of the storm is behind them. This is their story.

The first warning of an Atlantic hurricane or a Pacific typhoon is usually a ship report. Perhaps the captain of a passing freighter notices an unusually low pressure on his barometer early one morning. Quickly the word flashes out by radio to the United States Joint Hurricane Warning Service in Miami: "Low pressure of 28.2 inches at 18° North, 82° West, heavy swell, low overcast."

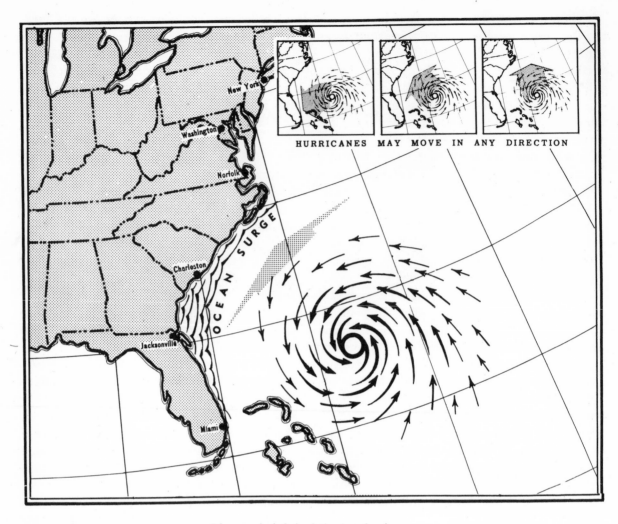

HURRICANES MAY MOVE IN ANY DIRECTION

Diagram of wind circulation in a hurricane.

The message causes the Warning Service to spring into action. Before dawn a United States Navy Super Constellation (WV-1) lifts its sleek nose into the blue from the Weather Squadron's base at Jacksonville, Florida. The hunt for the hurricane is on.

The time en route to the suspected area is spent in checking over plane equipment such as the radar, radio, and navigation gear. Once inside the storm belt, the navigator must prepare and the radio operator must send a position report every 15 minutes. This requires training, good equipment, and first-class co-ordination.

If the suspicious area is a true hurricane, the pilots and aerologists will generally become aware of this fact well before they reach the actual storm. Both sea and sky assume an appearance of strange unease. The first clouds are high cirrus fanning out in vaporous streaks. The sea looks confused with a nasty chop beginning to form. The air is soft with a queer wool-like mugginess.

The sky ahead takes on a haze which swiftly deepens into the famous "hurricane blue." Squadrons of low, loose scud clouds, flying swiftly before the storm, billow beneath the cirrus. The atmosphere becomes sticky and humid; the crewmen are hot and suffocated inside their cumbersome flight suits, life jackets and parachute harnesses.

Wind streaks appear on the water below, faint uncertain lines on the darkening sea. The aerologist compares them with the pictures of water patterns which he carries with him and estimates the wind at about 20 knots from the north. When the next position report is sent out, this information will go with it.

An atmosphere of tense waiting builds in the plane as it hurtles to the storm. The radioman feels like the loneliest man in the world as he listens to the distant astral sounds coming through his receivers.

The second mechanic checks the engines from the blisters near the tail. He notices a curious dryness in his throat and wonders vaguely why he didn't request duty on board a destroyer. He worries a little about the Number Two engine. Oil is blowing back from the breather tube in a sparkling black line. He makes a mental note to tell the first mechanic about it when they get back.

The navigator, bending over his charts, begins to feel slightly sick from the pitching and tossing of the plane. He munches the snack he brought for just such an emergency and braces himself against the navigation table.

The first big booming gusts of turbulence hammer the plane and both the pilots grab for the yoke at once. They have been flying on auto-pilot, and the blasts of wind catch them by surprise. The pilot flips off the auto-pilot switch and grins at the co-pilot as they wrestle with the controls. When the ship has settled down, they put the mixture control into auto-rich and increase the RPM's on the propellers in case they need more power. The pilot fumbles through his flight suit and comes up with a ragged-looking package of chewing gum. He offers a piece to the co-pilot who, busily concentrating on the instruments, shakes his head.

The technique of flying into the eye of a hurricane is in theory a very simple one, based on the law of storms. It merely requires that the pilot point the port (left) wing of the aircraft in the direction from which the wind is coming. When this is done properly the wind blows from the left side and the plane is blown in an arcking course directly into the eye of the storm. Departing is just as simple. The pilot manoeuvres his starboard (right) wing into the wind.

But there are several complications. In order for the pilot to keep the wind on the port side, the aerologist must be able to see the wind streaks on the water. This means that the plane must fly under the cloud base; since the hurricane clouds extend down to within 300 to 500 feet of the surface, flying in the violently turbulent air becomes very tricky and requires fast reactions from the crewmen. Often the plane will pass through patches where there is no ceiling at all and the scud extends right down to the surface. During those moments the pilot can do nothing except fly by his instruments and hope that the clouds will lift.

Another complication is produced by the tremendous pressure drop experienced on the flight into the storm. Since the aircraft's altimeters operate on an air-pressure principle, they are seriously affected by this change. The pressure altimeter, for example, indicates that the plane

A large beach-side building was broken in two by the force of a hurricane. The damage of hurricanes may cover a wide area. Generally, however, they do not produce the total devastation of a tornado.

is flying higher than it actually is. Thus, if the pilot were to believe the information furnished by his pressure altimeter, he would soon fly into the water.

In order to compensate for the error in the pressure altimeter, hurricane-reconnaissance aircraft are fitted with radar altimeters, which read correctly in spite of pressure changes.

Before heading into the storm, the pilots and aerologists will attempt to locate its weakest sector. They probe at it tentatively, like a bullfighter feeling out a new bull. If possible, they will penetrate one of the softer rear areas, though in order to do this they must actually start in ahead of the storm because of the mighty drifting movement of the wind.

Reconnaissance crews never know what to expect of a hurricane. If other crews have flown the storm before, they will do their best to describe it, pointing out its peculiarities and special dangers. However, during a period of 24 hours, its personality can make an abrupt about-face. A hurricane may be dry and smooth one day, violently turbulent and wet the next.

The hurricane winds of equal force blow around the hub in concentric, elliptical circles, which belly outward in the dangerous sectors. The actual penetration begins at the 60-knot circle where the aerologist orders the pilot to put the wind on his beam; from this point on, the

weatherman does the navigating for the crew, and their lives depend upon his decisions.

At the 60-knot circle, perhaps 75 miles from the eye, the rain lashes down in solid sheets, creating a union of sea and sky that blots out the horizon. Although the crew has inspected the aircraft carefully before the flight, replacing putty and gaskets, the water pours in and all aboard are soaked to the skin. Rivet-gun sounds batter their senses as the hull bends and strains, its metal skin popping under the fury of the storm. Ahead, the mighty torrent is wild and full of danger; the wind-torn seas reach up to the crewmen with ever-increasing fury.

The pilots scan the flickering instruments constantly. Rain cools the engines swiftly, and they watch the cylinder-head temperatures with great care. Experience has shown that aircraft engines suddenly quit when cylinder-head temperatures fall below 100° C. Periodically an engine takes a slug of water through its intake manifold, floods and cuts with a fearful cracking sound. The wind streaks on the sea wheel in a rapid counterclockwise fashion, and the pilot must continually alter course to keep the wind on his beam.

A few minutes before reaching the eye, the radar operator will see dense patches of weather which glow like solid land upon his scope. He will notify the crew that the worst is straight ahead.

By now the surface of the sea has the same appearance as the snow-covered ridges of Alaska. It is dead white; the waves are mountainous. The four-engined 120,000-pound bomber leaps like a wild thing under the sledgehammer blows of the wind. It stands on a wing one moment; its nose is pointed at the sea the next. The pilots fight desperately with yoke, rudder, and throttle to maintain in balance the delicate equation of flight.

Behind the pilots, the crew is caught within the dark cavernous hull, unable to see the storm or read the violent story of danger in the instruments. But they feel the shuddering fury through their bones and in their flesh. Their senses are filled with the murderous buffeting and the angry roar. Each one of them has become inwardly alone, isolated by the fury of the moment.

The rain blasts over the wings as though shot from a high-pressure fire hose, and the metallic structure twists and distorts under the abnormal strain. The pilot senses everything that happens to his craft with the intuition born of many flight hours. He knows that even in routine flying structural failures will sometimes occur which can fell a plane, but he disciplines himself against such thought for he cannot afford the luxury of fear.

Suddenly when it seems that the plane and the crew can stand no more, the roar subsides and they are literally tossed into the eye by the wind. An audible sigh passes through the ship. The trip out may be just as bad, perhaps even worse, but the crewmen feel the psychological advantage of having defeated the enemy. Relief is a physical thing which creeps into them slowly as hands relax their grip on equipment braces and faces lose the hollow look of strain.

The atmosphere of the eye is a misty, greenish

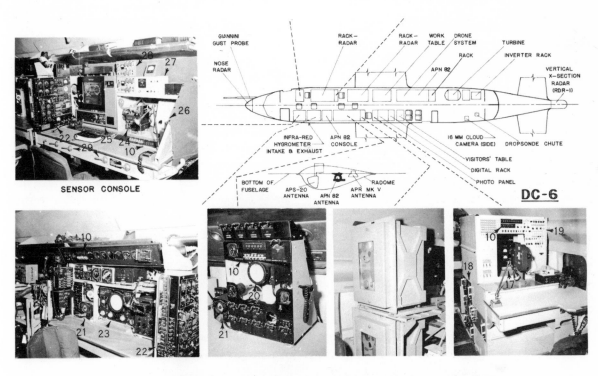

DETAILS OF A WEATHER RECONNAISSANCE PLANE

10. Time Display
18. Digital Card Drawers
19. Digital Console
20. APS-20E Repeater PP1 Scope
21. SCR-718 Radio Altimeter
22. Power Panel
23. APS-20E Remote PP1 Scope
24. Vortex Thermometer Amplifier and Indicator
25. MK V Radio Altimeter
26. Liquid Water Wire Instrument
27. Liquid Water Paper Tape Console
28. Silver Iodide Burner Controls
    and D-Value Computer

yellow. The plane is surrounded on all sides by dark olive-colored hurricane clouds; the sea looks wicked but confused. The radar operator notices that his scope is surrounded by a bright circle of weather echoes. He directs the pilot to steer courses which will keep the craft away from the ring of weather, and he carefully measures the diameter of the eye for the aerologist.

While the crew relaxes momentarily, the pilot circles in the eye. The navigators catch up on their charts and the aerologist makes up his "eye report," which will read approximately as follows:

HUREP NAVY EIGHT X EYE FIXED 18-20N: 82-10W AT 1410Z X HIGHEST WINDS 130 KNOTS FROM 080 DE-GREES X LOWEST PRESSURE 942 MILLIBARS X EYE WELL DEFINED BY RADAR X CIRCULAR IN SHAPE 16 MILES IN DIAMETER X RADAR COVERAGE BELIEVED FEASIBLE X ADVISE FUTURE RECONNAISSANCE AIRCRAFT TO AVOID NORTH QUADRANT X EXTREMELY TURBU-LENT X VERY WET X EYE OVER-CAST X RETURNING JAX.

As soon as the "eye report" has been trans-mitted and acknowledged, the crew is ready to start back. But the work of the hurricane-recon-naissance plane is not yet finished. The men receive a message to circumnavigate the disturb-ance on the 60-knot circle to determine the potential destructive area. It is not until hours later when they flash the message DISCON-TINUING CIRCUMNAVIGATING DUE FUEL EXHAUSTION that they can go home.

When they arrive home, they are bone-tired. Most of the plane's paint has been wiped clean from the wings and tail, bearing mute testimony to the intensity of the storm. Often fittings will be salt-encrusted showing that the aircraft was so low it actually flew within the surface spray.

As the men disembark stiffly from the aircraft, their eyes are red-rimmed and tired. Immediately upon landing, most of them are silent and ill-at-ease, as though unaccustomed to the strange familiarity of solid ground. They stand in groups quietly with little to say.

After their missions, the hurricane crews do not talk much about their work; when they do, it is in the humble, quiet tones that they might use in church or during the great events of their lives. They know that the terror and magnificence of the storm can never be imparted by words to other

Railway cars were derailed by a storm which struck Stoning-ton, Connecticut, on September 22, 1938. This storm later caused the damage at Buzzards Bay shown in the picture on page 70.

This 64-year-old woman was helped by the Red Cross after her home was wrecked by a hurricane.

men. About the hurricane they feel perhaps like Byron: *Oh night and storm and darkness! Ye are wondrous strong. Yet lovely in your strength.*

Based on the information from their "eye report" and postflight summary, the United States Weather Bureau issues its hurricane advisory report and the storm track forecast for the next 24 hours. All over the coast of Florida people nail storm shutters over their windows and otherwise prepare for the big blow as a result of this reconnaissance.

Man is no longer a moronic brute, and he no longer worships the hurricane as a god. He sends his aircraft out into the storm, plots its track on the blue-white radar scope, and blankets the country with notice of its coming. But no hurricane was ever subdued in the least fractional sense by any of his efforts. No hurricane has ever been caused to veer the merest trifle by his modern know-how. No hurricane has ever been predicted but only discovered by encounter. Nothing man has developed or dreamed of checks its terrible power. Great winds still ravage the earth and tidal waves demolish the coasts. Our efforts thus far have succeeded in but one phase: providing warning about nature's most dangerous catastrophe. Perhaps as the curtain of his ignorance lifts, man will control the sun-created hurricanes as today he is able to control the climate of his house. But until that day comes, there will still be a need for the hurricane-hunting planes and their valiant crews.

Aristotle as a youth, surrounded by the objects he was studying: music, plants, animals, the world. Along with other great works, Aristotle formulated the first theories of why the weather behaves as it does.

9. *Twenty-Five Thousand Prophets*

IN TODAY'S WORLD THE STRIDES TAKEN TO BUILD our civilization are rarely the result of a single gifted talent. The lonely inventor working in his basement and the scientific genius isolated in his ivory tower have vanished to be replaced by corps of skilled research teams in modern scientifically equipped buildings. Yet the great advances in man's knowledge have always been spearheaded by amateurs and all professions owe their origin to an amateur—for who can be a professional in a field not yet created?

Weather science or meteorology, as it was named by Aristotle, is no exception. Today many distinguished universities confer the degree of meteorologist upon skilled students. The basic laws have been established and the tools of the profession grow more complex daily. But in the Middle Ages no such science existed. Furthermore, most people then felt that there was no need for it. Aristotle, the fabulous Greek whose word was unchallenged, had settled the question of weather adequately and, it was thought, irrefutably, almost two thousand years before. His

book *Meteorologica*, written in 350 B.C., solved the weather problem for the civilized world for the next 20 centuries.

Aristotle based his theory of weather-prediction entirely on local conditions. He believed that tomorrow's storm could be foretold from symptoms that could be seen in the sky overhead today. He neglected entirely the effect of weather elsewhere in the world. And this purely visual method was used throughout the turbulent but dogmatic Middle Ages.

Only one flaw existed. Aristotle was wrong. By merely checking the weather against the forecasts, even the ordinary person could see that his forecasting technique did not work. But the temper of the age was such that the fault was always attributed to the observer, never to the theory of Aristotle.

Around the turn of the 17th century Galileo, the famous Italian astronomer and professional doubter, became entranced by the strange characteristics of the heavy metallic liquid called mercury. Much to his amazement, he found that a

74

A weather scientist draws a daily analysis chart of global weather patterns. Many such charts are drawn each day by weathermen all over the world.

few ounces of mercury, placed in a tube, expanded and contracted with heat and cold. His experiments resulted in the world's first thermometer, and upon this discovery the foundation of modern weather science was laid.

In 1643, Torricelli, a student of Galileo, observed another curious quality of mercury. When the liquid was placed in a bowl, not all of it ran out. In fact, a vertical column of about 30 inches remained. This held true for both fat and thin tubes, on hot days as well as cold—a truly mystifying fact. Torricelli noted, however, that the length of the column of mercury varied a few inches in height from day to day. Sometimes it climbed a little, and at other times it dropped. A true scientist, Torricelli recorded his findings carefully and went on to other experiments.

Blaise Pascal, the French physician, stumbled across Torricelli's findings in 1647 and wrote a letter concerning them to his brother-in-law, who was an ardent mountain climber. Pascal expressed the opinion that the only force which could keep the heavy mercury from running out of the tube was the weight of the air resting on the liquid in the bowl. He believed that the 30-inch column of mercury was equivalent to the total weight of the column of air above it. Since there would be less air above a mountain than there would be over a valley below, Pascal asked his brother-in-law to take one of Torricelli's mercurial tubes with him on his next mountaineering expedition. The young man did and wrote back excitedly that the mercurial column was over three inches shorter at the mountain's peak than it was at its base. Thus the barometer was born. Today it remains the most efficient method of measuring the weight of the column of air above us. Since most bad weather is associated with a decrease in air pressure, or low, as it is called, the barometer has become one of the most powerful tools of the weather forecaster.

From these beginnings the story of weather science unfolds. Slowly and reluctantly, the simmering, mobile envelope of air gave up its mysteries. The great trade winds which filled the sails of the 17th-century galleons in their search for commerce caused the final overthrow of Aristotle's weather theory. Seamen were forced to the belief that the atmosphere, like the rivers and oceans of the earth, was fluid and ever-moving. And this realization led to the knowledge that the islands of weather, as well as the spices of India and the gold of Peru, were navigated across the seas by the shifting winds. Relentlessly scientists pursued the mysteries of temperature and energy. And as the knowledge of the physical laws grew, it was applied to these mysteries until the complex relationships of the weather elements were fairly well understood.

Despite this increase in understanding, practically no advance was made in the science of weather forecasting for 200 years after the invention of the barometer. It was one thing to know that snow in Paris today would mean a blizzard in Berlin tomorrow, and quite another to use this knowledge effectively when the fastest means of communication was less speedy than the storm itself!

Then in 1844 Samuel Morse sent the world's first telegraphic message from Baltimore to Washington, D.C. The insurmountable difficulty had been overcome; for the first time it was possible to spread the news about the weather in time to make accurate forecasts. By 1850 detailed records of weather observations, taken with instruments, were being compiled and transmitted in many nations of the world. Through the study of such records, weathermen soon established their science, and the forecasting of weather moved from the realm of the amateur to that of the professional.

Almost from the start, weather science was separated into two major fields, which were given rather high-sounding names: *climatology* and *meteorology*. The difference between these fields is similar to that between the steam shovel and the garden spade. The climatologist is interested in the world-wide weather picture and the long-term weather trends. The meteorologist speaks only for his local area, and his forecasts extend no further than the coming week-end weather.

All weather phenomena are statistics for the climatologist. He compiles records of monthly, seasonal and yearly variations of temperature, pressure, rainfall, cloudiness, wind velocity and everything else that he can measure. He is mainly concerned with average conditions; a hurricane is just another freakish figure on a chart to him. Only if it were to last a year and upset the long-term balance would he become deeply concerned.

The demands for the services of a climatologist are enormous. The climatic factor enters into all human activities, and must be considered in intelligent planning, whether for industrial, residential, or agricultural purposes. An example of this is that the location of the United States Air Force Academy in Colorado Springs, Colorado, is directly attributable to a climatologist. Climate was a major factor in deciding the location of the cotton industry in the moist western half of northern England, and of the woollen industry in the drier eastern districts. Climatology teams will explore the weather of distant planets before the first spaceships descend upon their surfaces.

Rainfall, temperature, sunshine and humidity are major factors which have to be studied in relation to public health. Adequate water supply and proper drainage arrangements, which are among the first requirements for a healthy community, are dependent upon rainfall. The hydrologist must design his storage reservoirs so that their capacity is adequate to maintain the supply during periods of drought. The drainage engineer has to provide for the prevention of the flooding of streets by heavy thunderstorms. To meet these needs, rainfall records are analyzed, tabulated, and made available to the public by climatologists.

Also under the heading of health are included the important questions of hospital and sanatorium locations, and the selection of holiday resorts. On a broader scale, climatic records are valuable in the investigation of possible relationships between disease and particular weather conditions.

The farmer must guard against attempting to grow crops unsuited to the climate of his locality, and planting orchards on sites liable to frost; the exporter must allow for the effects of temperature and humidity on his shipments; and the builder is interested in maximum wind speeds and heavy rainfall. The climatologist may even be of value in a law court. If a farmer were to sue for the loss

A floating weather station is set adrift in the Atlantic. The tail at right gives the direction of the current.

"Owl Butte" in northeastern Arizona, a perfect likeness of a wise old bird, has been carved by the elements and time.

of a cow struck by lightning, the defendant might require proof that lightning was in fact reported at the time and place in question!

Sometimes the climatologist turns his attention from the sky and becomes interested in the earth itself. Climatology explains many absorbing facts about our landscape; thus, it enables the archaeologist to estimate the climate of the earth in prehistoric ages, for there is a close kinship between climate and earth topography. The United States, for example, is ridged by two mountain chains which separate the Great Plains of the central states from the coastal regions on either side. By the time the wet ocean winds pass over the mountains, their moisture is pretty much squeezed from them; therefore, rainfall is heaviest in the coastal states. Land erosion by water is a gentle process and the coastal countryside is characterized by rolling contours, sloping, rounded hills and many small streams. Because of the abundant rainfall, vegetation is rich and the forests grow dense. These in turn attract a thriving animal population which further enriches the earth.

Within the Great Plains water is more scarce and the landscape shows characteristic changes. The towering coastal forests give way to seas of prairie grass. The nature of animal life is quite different and few streams are encountered. In some regions where there is little rainfall, such as the southwestern states, the alkalinity of the soil, unwashed by rain, becomes very high. Vegetation is discouraged by these twin factors and dwindles away until the naked earth is left open to the scouring effect of wind erosion. The landscape is sharply jagged and weird shapes are cut from the stone by the gusts. Most of the candy-striped needles of rocks found in Death Valley are created by the sculpturing winds.

Many believe that the climatologist will ultimately refine his records and techniques to the point where he can predict the weather accurately for days, weeks and perhaps months in advance. These convictions are not merely based on a cherished hope. Astonishing, if little-known, miracles are being accomplished these days through the application of statistical laws. Quantum physics, which is used to unlock the continuously varying but nevertheless predictable secrets of the atom, leans heavily on statistics. Modern electronics has begun to apply statistical methods in the search for better communications and radar. Large-scale military operations are predicted with uncanny accuracy by statisticians far behind the battle lines. The vast storehouse of statistics which are collected daily about our weather may well result in ultimate victory for the climatologist in the fantastically complicated game of long-range prediction. But until that day arrives we must put our faith in the hands of the forecaster who does his best to tell us whether it will rain tomorrow and who will not even hazard a guess about next week.

Weather forecasting, like other physical sci-

A weatherman measures the rainfall using a standard 5-inch rain gauge. Many weather instruments have been standardized the world over to ensure that data can be used by others.

estimate of the probability of an event or sequence of events, and the assessment is made after weighing all available information and experience. It is, therefore, inevitable that a weather forecast should contain an element of uncertainty. Occasionally, it is true, the indications are so clear and unmistakable that certain features of the weather can be predicted for 12 or 24 hours ahead. But more frequently only an assessment, that is, a forecast, can be made. The important distinction between the words "forecast" and "prediction" is not always fully appreciated by listeners to or readers of weather forecasts.

Unfortunately, even during the best days, the weatherman is able to see a maximum of only 20 miles in any direction. Under the sodden clouds of bad weather, his visibility may be further restricted to almost zero. Buried in the dense, sometimes opaque layers of the lower atmosphere, he often cannot determine the weather ten miles away, much less the extent of storms brewing several hundred miles to the west. Yet these same storms may be over him almost before his next forecast is published.

It would seem a major advantage for the weatherman if he could only look down on the earth from above—say, from an altitude of 500 miles. Peering from such an observation post, he could watch the mighty hurricanes build and follow their courses across the oceans. The great frontal battlegrounds of the sky would stretch above the globe before his eyes, their lines accurately drawn, their intensity easy to predict. Huge sections of the earth would be blotted from his view by the bright, thin air-mass clouds. He would see the glowing miracle of snow follow the winter cold fronts across the land, and the green mantle of vegetation form quickly after the spring rains. Once and for all, he could solve the soundless mystery of the aurora borealis.

But even the weatherman operating far out in space would not be a perfect forecaster. Careful observation would soon reveal that some of the fronts hesitate as they move over the sphere, that many of the hurricanes take erratic, unpredictable paths, and often, inexplicably, that it stops raining although the same clouds still hover over the land. The shape and intensity of the storm areas often change without apparent reason. These things would cause the space observer to shake his head in perplexity, realizing that perhaps his greatest

ences, is based on two factors. One of these is instrumentation, such as the precious thermometer and barometer invented by the Italians of the 17th century, as well as the modern electronic devices like high-voltage radar. The second factor is visual observation. All sciences employ this technique. The weatherman, struggling to solve the complexities of an atmosphere in motion, has developed the art of observation to an incredible degree.

Incidentally, it is important to distinguish between a forecast and a prediction when talking of the weather. When a future event can be determined by exact laws, so that little or no element of uncertainty is left after the implications of the laws have been worked out, the event is held to be predicted with precision. It is in this sense that astronomers predict the time of the next full moon, or the next solar eclipse. On the other hand, when a future event (in this case the development of weather) can happen in several different ways and the laws governing it are not completely understood, the final estimate is a forecast. In this sense a forecast is a scientific

An ocean weather station "battles it out" during rough weather, and no one strays very far from the lifeline. Veteran weathermen tell of eating their dinner off the deck when the ship wallows like this in the sea.

advantage over his colleagues is that of distance from his critics.

In practice the modern weather observer does not have the visibility advantages of the space weatherman. Still, he has a method which allows him to analyze the world weather picture much more accurately.

The system is predicated upon the use of almost 5,000,000 weathermen throughout the world—some in uniform and others in civilian dress—all working together.

There are almost 25,000 weathermen in the United States alone, and these are the men who conduct the world-wide weather hunt on the North American continent and in the surrounding oceans. The hurricane-whipped waters of the Caribbean reflect the shadows of probing weather aircraft, and the mists of the foggy Aleutians are pierced by their boats. Thousands of weather stations dot the North American continent and its waters. All of these are linked by a gigantic communications network so that the start of a snowstorm in Nome, Alaska, is known in Panama City almost the minute it begins. At this very instant and during every hour of the year, weather observations are being taken by the tireless weather crew. The temperature, pressure, humidity, and winds are noted, coded, transmitted and analyzed until the mighty atmosphere yields its secrets far more completely than it would to any space observer.

This spiderweb of weather stations constitutes the modern weather machine and is the basis for weather prediction. It has existed only since 1914.

In that year Norway, a neutral country in

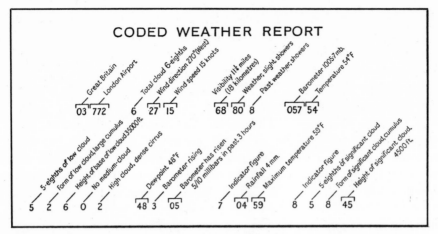

Great Britain
London Airport.
Total cloud 6-eighths
Wind direction 270°(West)
Wind speed 15 knots
Visibility 11¼ miles (18 kilometres)
Weather, slight showers
Past weather, showers
Barometer 1005.7 mb.
Temperature 54° F

03 772 | 6 | 27 15 | 68 80 8 | 057 54

5-eighths of low cloud
Form of low cloud, large cumulus
Height of base of low cloud 3500 ft.
No medium-cloud
High cloud, dense cirrus
Dew-point 48° F
Barometer rising
Barometer has risen 5/10 millibars in past 3 hours
Indicator figure
Rainfall 4 mm.
Maximum temperature 59° F
Indicator figure
5-eighths of significant cloud
Form of significant cloud, cumulus
Height of significant cloud, 4500 ft.

5 2 6 0 2 | 48 3 05 | 7 04 59 | 8 5 8 45

A coded weather report. Most countries use the same symbols so they can be read by weather-men of all lands.

World War I, was cut off from the weather reports of other countries and, more importantly, from the oceans which were being patrolled by warring fleets. To overcome this handicap, a dense system of weather stations was established each one only a few miles from the next. The Norwegian experiment was based on the research of a Norwegian physicist named Vilhelm Bjerknes. The results of the system became available to the world after the war ended. Bjerknes' pioneering, coupled with the subsequent findings of Tor Bergeron, Swedish meteorologist, and those of Jacob Bjerknes, son of Vilhelm, led to modern weather service. This system, which is now world-wide, relies upon the accurate information received from thousands of weather stations all over the world.

The observations made at most stations fall into two main groups—measurements made with instruments, and non-instrumental observations. The instrumental measurements include:

Barometric pressure, or "height" of the barometer.

Barometric tendency, amount in millibars, by which barometric pressure has changed in the last three hours.

Characteristic of tendency, type of change measured by barometric tendency in the last three hours, e.g. barometer has risen *or* barometer has fallen.

Temperature of the air.
Humidity, or moisture, of the air.
Direction and speed of wind.
Height of clouds.

The non-instrumental observations include:
Visibility.
Present weather and past weather.
Amount of cloud.
Types of cloud.
State of the ground.

These observations are made at many stations as a matter of routine at every observation hour. In addition, special thermometers are read four times a day to obtain the highest and lowest temperatures reached. The rainfall is also measured at the same times. A recording instrument for measuring the number of hours of sunshine each day exists at most stations.

At the smaller stations the schedule usually includes only the observations of weather, cloud, visibility and wind, which are the important factors for aviation purposes, the most important of all being the height of the base or lower surface, of the clouds.

Each set of observations yields an enormous amount of information, and it is the observer's duty to distill from it a brief message which can be sent quickly to the forecasters who are waiting for it. For this purpose use is made of an international figure code, called a "station model," copies of which are held at all observing and forecasting stations throughout the world. A great deal of information is packed into a short message by the use of this simple device.

So, the weatherman plots the station models upon his map at the points where the data for them was gathered. Next he draws a series of solid black lines which curve in odd swirls and circles across his charts. These are the *isobars,* or lines of equal barometric pressure. He finds the information for drawing them in the upper right-hand corner of the station model. The ancient barometer of Torricelli is still used as the basis for these readings.

Once the weatherman has drawn in his isobars, he locates the regions of highest pressure and labels these HIGH. The regions of lowest pressure he calls LOW. Once he has shaded the areas of rain and snow and sketched in the fronts, he has the weather map you will see in your newspaper in a few hours. This is called a *synoptic weather map* and although it has none of the reality and wondrous color which would be seen by the space weatherman, it is more accurate and informative than anything he could draw.

The synoptic weather map is deceptively simple. Much more can be deduced from it than the mere location of fronts, fog and rain. The isobars effectively form pipes through which the winds of the earth flow. If these lie close together the winds are generally strong. The effect is similar to that of the nozzle at the end of a fireman's hose.

The direction of the winds can be predicted also. In the Western Hemisphere, the winds blow clockwise around a high and flow out from the middle. The reverse is true for low-pressure areas.

While working on his map, the weatherman learns a great deal about the winds and storms over his country. He knows that if his country lies within the great band of prevailing westerly winds, the pressure systems and air masses on his map will travel from west to east. Experience has taught him that the great easterly movement covers about 500 miles a day in the summer and

700 miles a day in the winter. Thus he can look at the weather in a city hundreds of miles away and predict roughly what the weather there will be on the following day.

However, accurate weather prediction is never quite that easy.

The westerly flow high in the stratosphere may be predicted accurately enough to be used advantageously by high-flying aircraft, but unfortunately the flow at the earth's surface is complicated. Mountain ranges jut into the winds and displace their currents. Vertical air currents rise from the unevenly heated land and blend with the lower air. New fronts suddenly grow; inexplicably, old ones will lie dormant for days.

The net result is that the weatherman must exploit his training, his experience and his powers of observation to the limit. But so skilled have our observers become that despite the changing patterns in the sky, their predictions are about 85% correct.

The United States Weather Bureau has located two automatic weather stations on uninhabited islands in the Bahamas east of Florida. These robots are equipped with elaborate telemetric devices which transmit barometric pressure, wind direction, and wind velocity by radio. United States Weather Bureau offices at Miami and Key West pick up the signals which are transmitted to a wax-paper tape. Each station has a time-clock

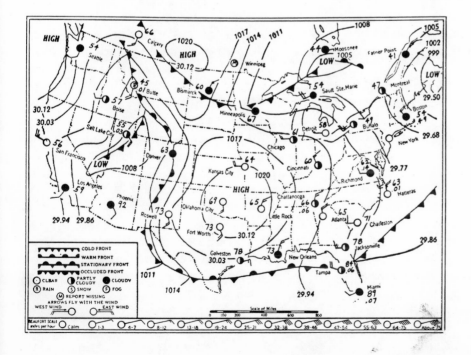

A standard weather map gives an accurate picture of the weather and provides an indication of what the weather will be for the next 24 hours.

arrangement which puts the station on the air at 15-minute intervals every three hours.

Our weather-forecasting machine and its mechanisms are barely 100 years old. Many original copies of the weather tools described in this chapter have not yet worn out. The modern concept of weather theory is no older than a middle-aged man. Yet in this brief period our scientists have successfully challenged the mysteries of the weather laws and have found the keys to secrets which had remained untouched for thousands of years. Today's progress is concerned chiefly with understanding and predicting the motion of the atmosphere. But throughout the story of science, understanding has been but the first step to the creation of a new technique, a new system. Einstein's insight was the prelude to the atomic reactor. Newton's conjecturing led to the building of our modern bridges and dams. It appears inevitable that some day man will remake the weather according to his own desires. As we will see later, the efforts already made in that direction indicate this day is but a brief moment away as time is measured by the historians.

The daily conference at a regional forecaster's office in England. Unfortunately, such meetings do not decide the weather—merely forecast it.

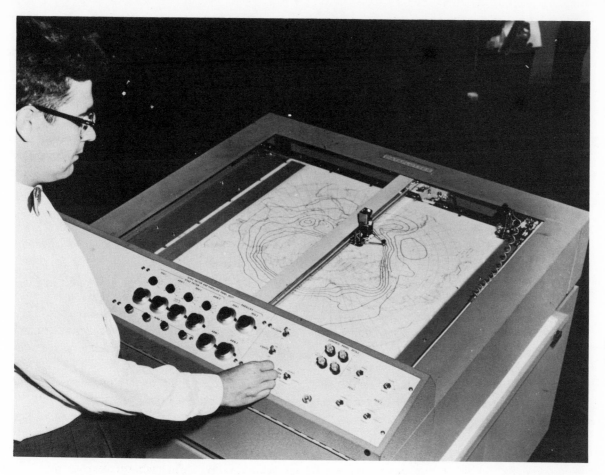

An electronic computer-plotter drawing a weather map.

10. The Robot Forecaster

CAPTAIN HOWARD T. ORVILLE WAS FORMERLY THE top United States Navy weatherman and chairman of President Eisenhower's Rain-Making Study Committee. Speaking before the American Institute of Electrical Engineers, he said that the tremendous property losses, the many highway deaths, and the suffering caused to millions of persons during winter months by ice and sleet storms could be greatly reduced through electronic weather prediction. He also stated that radar storm-detection units, co-ordinated with other key equipment placed at about 35 points around the country, could predict to the minute the arrival of a storm, its intensity and its duration.

He further stated: "Electronic forecasting, combined with data already available through existing United States Weather Bureau facilities, could predict, for example, that it will snow in Ann Arbor, Michigan, from 2:00 P.M. tomorrow until 3:45 P.M., and how much."

According to Captain Orville, the use of radar tracking in hurricanes has cut deaths from these storms by 98%. He believed it would take ten years to set up a nationwide electronic weather-warning system, but the resulting saving of millions of dollars in storm damage and thousands of lives would be well worth the time and the cost.

The 35 electronic weather stations which he contemplated would contain the following instruments: (1) a storm-detection radar displaying a picture of all the rain, snow, sleet or hail over an area of several thousand miles around the station; (2) a radar set which provides the cloud-base and cloud-top height information continuously for all cloud layers passing over the station; (3) recording equipment such as radiosonde balloons which automatically transmit data on temperature, pressure, humidity and other facts from altitudes up to 100,000 feet; (4) radar and television units capable of relaying weather conditions from one station to another; (5) electronic computers which combine the data from each station with all known weather information gathered throughout the Northern Hemisphere.

Under some conditions, Captain Orville added, radar-equipped aircraft would be used to supplement the ground units. Each station would be manned by two radar technicians and ten or twelve weather observers.

Fantastic as these schemes may appear, Captain Orville knew that there are sound principles behind them and that many strides have been taken to perfecting the equipment necessary to do this job.

The magical electronic eye of radar has already demonstrated its ability to seek out storms and clouds, just as it was able to detect the snorkel of enemy submarines in World War II. Actually,

radar does not see the storm but receives its echo from the air-borne masses of rain, snow, sleet or hail. Millions of these air-borne particles reflect the pulsing energy to rebound and to be recorded upon the radarscope. Radarmen have learned how to interpret these telltale images with the result that trained observers can now predict the precise location and extent of weather storms from them.

The major airlines were the first to be interested in the freakish ability of radar to locate storms. Their chief concern was that of safety. The extreme turbulence found in some thunderclouds has long troubled aviators. Almost any airport can produce an airman who will testify from personal experience that flying through thunderstorms almost cost him his life. Such men describe violent up-currents which sent their planes hurtling up at express speeds and turbulence severe enough to flip multi-engined aircraft upside down.

These reports with their emphasis on safety provided the basis for the airlines' desire to devise some method of avoiding such storms. Aside from the commercial value of the aircraft and its equipment, there was the commercial value of its passengers. An airline whose routes continually passed through thunderstorm areas became accustomed to dealing with sick and hostile

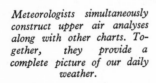

Meteorologists simultaneously construct upper air analyses along with other charts. Together, they provide a complete picture of our daily weather.

The United States Weather Bureau uses storm detection radar scanning equipment to study the development of storms as far as 250 miles away. Using radar, the operator can analyze details by magnifying a small area.

passengers. The problem was by no means a small one. Although the thunderstorm is a rare phenomenon to ground-dwellers in many parts, it is encountered frequently on long aircraft flights. For example, the summer of 1961 was not remarkable for its thunderstorm activity in the United States, yet for 69 consecutive days there was a turbulent thunderhead somewhere along the airline route between Denver, Colorado, and Omaha, Nebraska.

Prior to the use of radar, only one alternative was open to the airline pilots. If a thunderstorm was reported along their route, a detour was necessary with a resulting loss in time, fuel, and profit. In 1946, American Airlines conducted a series of tests with World War II equipment to determine the effectiveness of radar as a storm-warning aid. The results were startlingly successful.

American Airlines engineers quickly determined that radar echoes were received mainly from rain and hail. Tests showed that light rain produced a weaker picture on their scopes than heavy rain; they were even more successful in indicating hail.

World War II equipment was not the final answer, however. Although the pilot was able to locate the storm front and estimate the type of precipitation, he could not determine the depth of the storm. Such determination was extremely desirable, since the pilot who could probe the extent of a storm was able to pick the most direct route through it. Thus, if he found it possible to pass quickly through a mild sector, it was more advantageous than flying a costly detour of perhaps many hundreds of miles.

The airline company therefore assigned a team of electronic engineers to work on the problem. These men solved it by developing a new radar. The new radar underwent extensive tests during 1954 and achieved spectacular results. Its pulses penetrate the storm front and define the area

Unpleasant weather at a crossroads of the Atlantic Ocean as men aboard weather ships often see it. Few people have more trying jobs; black skies, high seas and winds of gale force often lay siege to ships for days on end.

beyond. The thundercloud emerges on the scope as a dappled pattern of strong and weak echoes. By choosing a path through the mild area, the pilot can now avoid the dangerous turbulence. Repeated flights have shown that the pilots do not need to fly more than 25 miles out of their way. Instead, they can thread their path through corridors in the storm which are often less than five miles wide, and except for mild bumpiness, they arrive unscathed on the other side.

The lessons learned by the airlines were not lost upon the weathermen. They readily employed the new apparatus in establishing the renowned Joint Hurricane Warning Service. Today the flight crews of both the United States Air Force and Navy who penetrate the hurricanes of the Atlantic and the typhoons of the Pacific Ocean

depend largely on radar for the successful completion of their missions. On their way in and out of these mighty storms, they are guided by radar around the ominous areas of high turbulence. Once within the eye, radar enables them to search out the necessary information concerning its size and shape. At night the hurricane is tracked continuously by radar aircraft which fly in an orbit near the edge.

The use of radar by the Joint Hurricane Warning Service is but one military application. Accurate short-range weather prediction is vital to ground forces in wartime. History is filled with tales of lost battles caused by unexpected weather changes which turned roads into quagmires and fields into swamps.

With this in mind, the United States Army

Signal Corps has sponsored intensive weather research work at the Massachussetts Institute of Technology since World War II. A few of the first radar sets designed for weather study by this project are now being put into operation. These units are expensive, but they are well worth the cost. Cloud forms can be distinguished upon their scopes, and even minor amounts of rainfall can be located and forecast with precision.

As each day passes, more uses are found for radar as a tool for the weathermen. Industrial firms near the hurricane coasts have found it profitable to build their own weather stations. The Dow Chemical Company in Freeport, Texas, has two plants located on the flat lowlands near the Gulf of Mexico. Before the use of radar these plants had to stop operation whenever there was a hurricane in the Gulf. Although most of these storms never came near Freeport, no means existed of predicting their path. In eight years, suspended operation cost the company over $2,000,000. In 1948 Dow installed a search radar. Not only has this unit ended unnecessary work stoppages but it has located and tracked several hurricanes, which previously were undetected and which did pass through Freeport. Today Dow is one of many industrial agencies co-operating with the Weather Bureau in hurricane reconnaissance.

After the usefulness of radar was demonstrated in locating hurricanes, many weathermen speculated that it could also be used to give the alarm at the approach of the death-dealing, violent tornado. During the spring of 1953 the cities of San Angelo and Waco, Texas, were struck by vicious twisters, and the state of Texas sought a means of warning against further catastrophes. A meeting of federal and state representatives was convened. Before the session ended, a new adventure in community enterprise and self-help was launched.

The United States Weather Bureau offered to make some of its war-surplus radar available to Texas communities if the local governments would provide money to convert them to weather radars. Texas A & M College agreed to undertake the conversion, and a fund-raising campaign got off to a fast start. By the spring of 1954 12 out of 15 Texas cities signed contracts for financing the radar installations, and two sets were in action. The spring of 1955 found the tornadoes of the Texas Plains added to the growing list of

storms under full radar surveillance. Captain Orville's dream has already begun to assume a semblance of reality.

The great advance in technical knowledge which grew out of World War II and which resulted in radar, supersonic aircraft, and guided missiles produced another unique device: the digital computer or automatic brain. A digital computer is a fantastically complex electronic machine based on the principles of the adding machine found in most business offices. Its resemblance to this machine is as remote as the H-bomb's likeness to the bow and arrow. It can perform more calculation in five minutes than an expert working with an adding machine could do in 60 years. Until very recently, the chief application of this incredible device was the solution of the more complex problems of higher mathematics. This situation changed when WBAN, usually called "wayban," was established.

WBAN stands for the initials of the Weather Bureau, Air, Navy. It is a composite organization located in Washington, D.C., established for the purpose of pooling, analyzing and distributing weather information to its members. The United

This type of computer is used to aid in the prediction of weather. Weathermen feel that computers will become increasingly important to weather scientists.

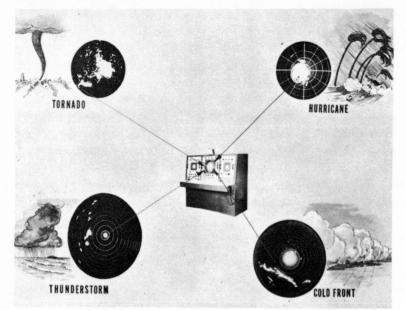

Radar has become one of the most valuable tools of the weatherman. This picture shows some of the information which it provides.

States Navy requires this information for its ships at sea, the United States Air Force for its planes, and the Weather Bureau for the civilian public.

The co-operation of these three meteorological groups in pooling their information was furthered in 1947 when the United States Congress joined them officially. From that time on not only was weather information shared but the research effort of all three groups was integrated.

Early in their union, the weather partners planned and committed themselves to a bold step in mastering the unknown. They proposed to build a machine which would be capable of forecasting the weather with greater accuracy than any human forecaster!

A vivid example of the electronic brain's potentiality as a means of predicting future events was demonstrated during the 1952 presidential election in the United States. One of these electronic wizards was set up to predict the final vote on the basis of early returns. On election night the early results were given to the machine. The thousands of relays clicked, the tapes hummed and the electronic tubes glowed. Finally, on the electric typewriter, which is the wizard's mouth, the prediction was tapped out: Eisenhower by an avalanche.

The assembled scientists were aghast. The election was supposed to be close. Even the most devout Republican could not believe that the margin would be as large as the results indicated.

They were quite sure there was a short circuit in the giant brain or that the information had been fed to the machine improperly. In any case, they announced that the machine was out of order. The difference between the final vote tabulation and the machine's prediction was amazingly small. In the elections since then, the computer has achieved a considerable reputation for reliability and accuracy.

The method used to predict elections is quite simple, but requires the machine to perform a feat of memory far beyond the capability of a thousand men. The results of many past elections are fed into the mechanism. These are stored in the thousands of tubes and cells within the electronic brain, making it a more experienced forecaster than any politician. During an election these past results are compared with the current trend to arrive at a sound prediction.

To imagine the use of this machine for predicting the weather, all we must do is substitute weather information for votes. In place of the key results, the data from weather stations would be fed into the machine. The idea was not fantastic in the sense of science-fiction, but was very difficult to put into operation.

The United States Joint Chiefs of Staff supported the project, military research funds were made available and the Institute for Advanced Study at Princeton, New Jersey, was instructed to do the job. Six years of intensive experimentation and a great deal of money were required, and by 1952 the first model of a weather-predicting mechanical brain was in experimental operation.

The Princeton group began its operation very slowly. Theirs was a new world of science to explore, and every move was cautiously planned. Many observers doubted that man could ever uncover the intricate laws of the gigantic, mobile atmosphere. Dr. Jule G. Charney and his associates embarked upon the project confidently. The first milestone was reached when the scientists devised theoretical methods of predicting the motion of the atmosphere at one altitude along a single circle of latitude.

From this they progressed to the infinitely more complicated problem of predicting the atmospheric currents over a large part of the United States. Next they expanded the study to include air movements over three altitudes. Today they can handle the gyrations of the atmospheric streams within five levels over the United States. In 1952 their electronic brain, designed by Professors John Von Neumann and Julian Bigelow, was ready.

This machine based its prediction on the data fed into it from 768 weather stations which gathered the local weather data at exactly the same time. On the basis of the information received, the electronic brain went into action. It performed 750,000 multiplications, 10,000,000 additions and subtractions, and executed 30,000,000 distinct orders given by its robot controls. In 48 minutes the forecast was ready. The same forecast, made by hand, would have taken hundreds of years, somewhat late for the morning edition of the local newspapers.

Each year improvements have been made in the 1952 machine. Today it can handle close to 2,000 separate weather stations. The data to be fed into it is gathered from all over the United States. One more step to Captain Orville's dream has been achieved.

The atmosphere does not yield its secrets easily, and the present forecasting machine is not perfect by any means. But the results obtained from the electronic brain have been most encouraging. Captain John McKillip, U.S.N., head of the

"Soundings" of the upper atmosphere to obtain precise atmospheric information are taken at various times during the day at such places as this aircraft carrier, far out at sea.

Navy Aerology Branch, recently stated: "Results of machine forecasts are significantly better than the best human predictions now available."

In order to determine the capabilities of their weather-predicting machine, Professor Charney and his associates have tried their hand at predicting the freakish and unexpected storms of past years. Such forecasts afford the Princeton team a method of checking the accuracy of their computations. The scientists scrupulously included only the official United States Weather Bureau data which would have been available to them before the storm. They tested their technique by predicting three eastern seaboard snowstorms which completely surprised the weather experts at the time of their actual occurrence.

These included the snowstorm of November, 1950, the storm of November, 1952, and the violent blizzard of November, 1953. None of these was even faintly anticipated by local weathermen until it appeared overhead.

The first two storms were predicted with astonishing accuracy by the electronic machine, much to the gratification of the observers. The third forecast, however, failed. A second run with the same data produced an identical result: the machine could find no storm. Instead of taking an axe to the machine, the scientists began a painstaking check of all their data. During this process it was found that the information collected on November 5th by a weather ship stationed between Norfolk, Virginia, and Bermuda had not been utilized by the United States Weather Bureau. This additional weather information was fed into the machine, which came up with a concise, accurate prediction of the storm.

This episode clearly illustrates the enormity of the problem faced by scientists working on the machine-forecasting project. This machine, like all others, is no more reliable than the facts which are fed into it. The difficulty of sampling accurately the world's atmosphere is huge, but the scientists will never admit that it is impossible.

Jule Charney and his technical team do not believe they can ever eliminate the local forecaster. But they do feel that their electronic computer will give accurate area forecasts. This will allow the local weatherman to spend more time pin-pointing his particular section, basing his local forecasts on the electronic-brain predictions and the subtle regional influences which only he knows.

The progress made so far is incredible when we realize that radar and electronic-computing devices are only about 15 years old. Already they have influenced drastically our techniques of weather forecasting. There is no means by which we can predict man's ultimate ability to search out the hidden secrets of the air around us, but we can find the shaping of future events in Captain Orville's prophetic words. The accuracy of weather prediction will be vastly increased; the exact time of rainfall will be forecasted as precisely as we now can foretell the rise and fall of the tides. Slowly we are postulating the laws of atmospheric motion. From our knowledge of these we will build our machine and extend our forecasts in time to a month and then perhaps a year ahead. We will learn to track the tornado before it is hurled down upon us; we will know exactly when and where the cyclone will strike. Then, armed with this knowledge, we will set forth to conquer the weather we now predict.

The Tiros weather satellite, one of the most complex electronic systems yet sent into space, is shown here in assembly.

11. The Weather Moons

STANDING ON THE SURFACE OF OUR EARTH, WEATHER-men are able to observe no more than a micro-scopic segment of the total atmosphere. Also, the modest portion which they can see is distorted and warped by the very weather phenomena they seek to forecast. For these reasons it is extremely difficult to understand the global pattern of the great weather systems which sweep over us, and we are constantly surprised. Weather predictions only a few hours old often suddenly go awry.

How much better for the weatherman if he could only move outside the atmosphere and make his predictions from some far-off vantage point such as the moon, aided, of course, by a few pedestrian numbers such as the surface tempera-ture, pressure and humidity!

Weathermen have long been among those who yearned for space travel with all the zeal of starry-eyed visionaries. When space enthusiasts realized their ancient dream of orbiting man-created moons, weathermen were quick to applaud their achievements and beat the drum for a weather observation platform in space.

With the launching of the United States' Tiros I on April 1, 1960, weathermen were provided with a satellite's eye-view of the atmosphere, and the United States had taken the first giant step towards construction of a useful space weather station. It is perhaps significant that the launching vehicle for this peaceful space object was the warlike Thor medium range ballistic missile.

Dr. Morris Tepper is the director of the

United States' National Aeronautics and Space Administration's meteorological projects. Not long ago, he recounted some of the events of that first weather satellite launching: "After the spacecraft was placed in orbit, the big question was—what would we see? Would we have pictures? Would the pictures be merely curiosities or would they show significant cloud formations?"

A team of meteorologists under Dr. Sigmund Fritz had stationed themselves at Fort Monmouth, New Jersey, where the United States Army had a powerful radio receiving station that would provide the first weather satellite readout.* Dr. Tepper remained in Washington. After Tiros I had transmitted its first data, Dr. Fritz called Dr. Tepper and informed him that the pictures were received.

"But what do they show?" asked Dr. Tepper impatiently.

"Clouds," was the answer.

"What is the shape of the clouds? Can we see land? Are there any details?" Dr. Tepper began pouring the questions at his colleague.

Dr. Fritz finally broke in to say: "If you will wait a moment, I will send them to you."

Using an electronic transcribing machine called a Photofax, these first weather satellite pictures were transmitted to Washington in about five minutes. As Dr. Tepper was to say later: "They were wonderfully detailed pictures of the earth showing remarkably clear views of its cloud coverage. From that day forward, there never has been a doubt of the practicability and usefulness of weather satellites."

However, Tiros I was, at best, a crude observation post. To remain stable in its orbit 450 miles above the earth, the satellite maintained a spin rate of nine revolutions per minute with the result that its two cameras were pointed away from the earth most of the time. The resolving power of the instruments was poor and the electrical power was limited by the capacity of the 9,200 solar cells which covered the outer surface of the satellite and converted the sun's energy into electricity for the nickel-cadmium batteries. Tiros I was shaped like a giant pillbox, 42 inches in diameter and 19 inches high. It weighed 270 pounds or about as much as the first Soviet satellite, Sputnik I, launched almost three years before.

The cameras were actually television transmitters and their pictures were recorded on tape.

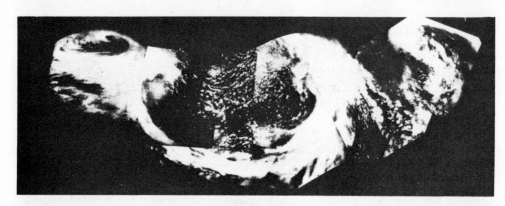

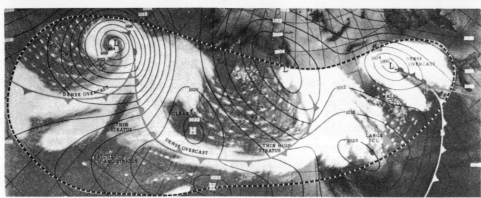

Here is a mosaic of Tiros weather pictures (top) compared with a daily weather map showing a clear outline of cloud formations and frontal patterns.

*Readout is simply the reception of information on earth by digital or analog display transmitted from a body (balloon, satellite, etc.) sent by man into space.

TIROS
METEOROLOGICAL SATELLITE

RECEIVING ANTENNA
SOLAR CELLS
IR PACKAGE
MAGNETIC ORIENTATION COIL

TV CAMERA
TAPE TRANSPORT
TV CAMERA
TRANSMITTING ANTENNA

SNOW OVER HIMALAYAS

SPAIN & STRAIT OF GIBRALTAR STORM OVER NORTH ATLANTIC

ICE IN GULF OF ST. LAWRENCE

OCCLUSION OVER NORTH ATLANTIC

A vigilant weather satellite orbits the earth.

When the satellite passed over either of two ground stations at Fort Monmouth, New Jersey, or Kaena Point, Hawaii, the taped signals were transmitted to the waiting weathermen in much the same way that pre-recorded television programs are re-broadcast. The weather over the ground stations, however, was transmitted "live."

One of the Tiros I television cameras was designed to take wide-angle pictures, covering an area of 800 square miles. The other camera surveyed an area 70 miles on a side but provided much more detail. Within 60 hours after Tiros I was launched, actual pictures of the global weather patterns only six hours old were being interpreted and analyzed by weathermen at the National Meteorological Center at Suitland, Maryland. For the first time, scientists could compare their guesses of cloud patterns with actual pictures of the real thing.

During the more than two months of its useful life, Tiros I generated 23,000 weather pictures. It would be impossible to place a tag on the value of the information obtained from this first weather-eye, small and unsophisticated though it was. Tiros I demonstrated the feasibility of a weather satellite. It made important scientific measurements of the atmosphere which could be used in day-to-day analysis and forecasting operations. In addition, all countries of the world have access to the Tiros data and it has become an international co-operative meteorological project.

Tiros I and its younger brothers have already produced almost 1,000,000 weather pictures, convincing proof of successful weather satellite operation. Perhaps no other scheme in the far-flung space effort has resulted in such immediate and continued success.

On page 92 is a mosaic of photographs viewed

by Tiros I. Below, the clouds have been drawn in their proper geographic location. The close relationship between the cloud positions and the weather fronts is truly remarkable.

The first four Tiros satellites were orbited with inclinations of less than 50°. In other words, they travel over the surface of the earth between the latitudes of 50° North and 50° South. These limits correspond approximately to the coverage of Tiros weather observations. The next satellite, Tiros V, was launched into a high inclination orbit of 58° with a resulting increase in coverage. The scientists of England and the Scandinavian countries were particularly pleased with this change since it afforded them the opportunity of observing the weather over these countries. In addition, the expanded coverage allowed weathermen to observe the ebb and flow of the sea ice at edges of the polar icecaps.

The United States' sixth Tiros satellite was rocketed into orbit on September 18, 1962. Tiros VI was originally scheduled for launching later in 1962 in an orbit of greater inclination. However, one of the television cameras in Tiros V failed and satellite weather information was vitally needed prior to astronaut Walter Schirra's orbital attempt, particularly since this was the first United States flight designed for recovery in the Pacific Ocean. Tiros satellites have provided weather forecasting support for all United States

Tiros VIII photographed Hurricane Hilda as it moved towards the Gulf Coast. President Lyndon B. Johnson said, "Hilda was probably the best tracked and most accurately predicted hurricane in history."

manned space flights since astronaut Alan Shephard's sub-orbital leap of May 5, 1961.

Tiros VI was also needed for an additional function which has rapidly become one of the most important Tiros jobs: hurricane hunting. Satellites have proved their worth in searching out and providing early warnings of these destructive storms. Tiros VI was the last satellite launched which would survey the hurricane belt around the earth's middle during the 1962 season.

Between April 1, 1960, and January 22, 1965, a total of nine Tiros satellites were launched, all of them were successful, and recording the data which they have transmitted back to earth has required hundreds of miles of magnetic tape. Since 1963 no day has passed during which weather scientists have not used Tiros data in making their forecasts.

Total world coverage by weather satellites began when the first Nimbus satellites were launched by the United States in 1964. Instead of following an inclined path near the equator, Nimbus is placed in a polar orbit so that it passes over both poles during every revolution. Nimbus circles the earth at an altitude of 600 miles and its three television cameras cover a rectangular area about 500 by 1,500 miles. These dimensions were elected so that the area covered by successive orbits would join, thus providing continuous coverage of the earth's surface. The Nimbus

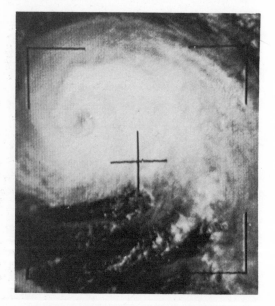

Nimbus' infra-red system produced this photograph of a hurricane over Chesapeake and Delaware Bays.

polar orbit provides complete world coverage as the earth rotates beneath the satellite. Nimbus I was launched on August 28, 1964.

Since Nimbus passes over the poles on every orbit, the ideal Nimbus readout station would have a location at either the North or South Pole. For obvious reasons, a polar data acquisition station has many disadvantages. The first Nimbus station has been installed at Fairbanks, Alaska, and it is capable of reading out all except four of the fourteen daily Nimbus orbits. A second station is located at Rosman, North Carolina, to read out the remaining four. Nimbus satellites can cover every point on the earth once every 12 hours, once in the daytime and once at night.

Unfortunately, this frequency of observation is still not adequate for some of the weatherman's problems. Many violent thunderstorms run their turbulent courses in less than five hours. Tornadoes have extremely short lives, lasting minutes only.

With one Nimbus satellite in orbit, hurricanes and all large cyclonic storms can be observed easily. Two Nimbus satellites will improve matters somewhat since they would cover the earth's surface every six hours. Still, many storms would escape undetected. Best of all, the weatherman would like a satellite which could paint a continuous picture of the world weather patterns in the same way that television continuously shows the action of a sports event. In addition, he would like to have the option of switching to enlargements of those areas which are most interesting at the moment.

Does this sound like a great deal to ask? Well, perhaps, but the technique for providing most of what the weatherman wants is available, and already such a satellite is on the drawing boards.

It is being designed for launching into a synchronous equatorial orbit. A satellite in such an orbit appears to remain stationary over a planned area on the earth's equator. This arises from the fact that a satellite in a circular orbit 22,300 miles distant from the earth must complete an orbit every 24 hours. Since the earth completes a revolution about its axis in the same period of time, such a satellite appears to be stationary in the sky. The synchronous weather satellite is still in a preliminary design phase.

From its 22,300 mile perch above the earth, each such satellite will provide continuous sur-

A series of cloud pictures of the Caribbean taken by the Nimbus I weather satellite.

An earth-bound antenna receives Tiros weather pictures.

About seven orbits of data can be obtained by the ground stations each day, which means about 450 pictures. As the photos are received they are displayed directly on an instrument called the photokinescope which is nothing more or less than an ordinary television screen. The pictures are then photographed on 35 mm. film. Within half an hour after the Tiros has surveyed a portion of the earth from its distant station 450 miles above us, the film can be processed and in the hands of a Center meteorologist. Pictures from remote areas, such as Africa, will take somewhat longer with the present equipment.

There have been some problems with each of the United States weather satellites, but on the whole, performance has been excellent. Of the 23,000 Tiros I pictures about two-thirds were interesting to weathermen. There were only two major failures in the system. Between orbits 22 and 572 the narrow-angle camera did not work. Inexplicably it began functioning again during orbit 573. Fortunately, the wide-angle camera was far more useful in furnishing weather data. After 78 days of operation, the satellite died because a relay failed, causing the batteries to discharge, thus draining the Tiros of all its electrical power. However, the beacon on Tiros I still transmits when it is in sunlight and the tracking stations are still able to plot its course. It will be many centuries before the first weather satellite will be slowed sufficiently by friction so that it will sink into a fiery, meteor-like grave in the upper atmosphere.

The Tiros satellites will be most helpful in predicting the weather for those areas which have the fewest surface weather stations. The Southern Hemisphere is 80% oceans, and observational data is also scarce in the tropical regions. These areas where the least is known about local and regional weather effects will receive a large share of the benefits from the weather satellites.

Perhaps the best statement concerning the use of these new and glamorous tools was made by the late Dr. Harry Wexler, Director of Research for the United States Weather Bureau, at the opening of the 1961 International Meteorological Satellite Workshop: "For the first time meteorologists have an observing device which, like the atmosphere, is global in extent. Meteorologists, traditionally, have pieced together visual observations and those from instruments and radar to

veillance of about one-quarter to one-third of the earth's surface. It will have at least two television cameras. The wide-angle version will provide a viewing angle much like that of a conventional home film projector. The other camera will show a great deal of detail but will have a narrow field of view. This high resolution camera will be directable on command so that a selected area can be observed at any time. Based on the big-picture data obtained by the wide-angle system, the narrow-field instrument will search the surface with a magnifying glass to seek out the areas of greatest interest to weathermen.

The problem of acquiring data from a satellite is a new one and the Tiros Data Acquisition Centers are quite different from conventional weather stations. A large antenna, 60 feet in diameter, is used to receive the signals from the weather-eye.

Since the satellite is designed to take pictures on command from the ground, the United States Weather Bureau advises the Acquisition Center of the areas where photographs of the clouds are desired. The Acquisition Center then makes up a scheme and sends it to the satellite. This plan may require the Tiros to take pictures immediately or at some predetermined time in the future. The Center also controls data readout.

At the Automatic Picture Transmission ground station in Maryland, the meteorological technician points the antenna towards the signal of the satellite as it rises over the horizon. As soon as reception begins, the technician hears a signal that assures him that the facsimile recorder has begun the automatic recording of the satellite's pictures. He follows the satellite's orbit with pre-distributed orbit information and by monitoring the strength of the signal. This gives weathermen a swift and permanent record of cloud formations.

construct synoptic charts over large areas the size of a continent and, more recently, the size of a hemisphere. In so doing, meteorologists have had to interpolate and extrapolate over areas where observations are sparse or missing, particularly over oceans and other uninhabited areas. The earth-orbiting satellite, by its ability to photograph the cloud cover and measure the outgoing radiation patterns, takes advantage of the natural weather maps which nature has already provided."

It would be most difficult to estimate the ultimate impact of the weather satellites on our daily lives. On some not-so-distant evening we are certain to turn on our television sets and something far different from the usual weatherman with his weather charts and pointer will flash to life on the screen before us. We will see a faithful reproduction of the world and local weather as viewed by the cold and distant eye of a Nimbus weather satellite keeping eternal watch from outer space. Pictures will be available to all men everywhere, to the farmer worried about his crops deep in the Ural Mountains and to the ship captain on the Indian Ocean. All of us will have become our own weathermen and, hopefully, we will all be drawn closer together by the international spirit of co-operation which is a keystone of the weather satellite project.

In looking at the future of weather moons, President Johnson said: "As satellites extend man's vision into new dimensions, weather forecasting will make major advances as a science, until we see reliable predictions a season ahead. This will have far-reaching benefits for all."

British landing craft are hammered by the waves at Normandy.

12. The Invisible Army

IN THE DEVELOPMENT OF THE MODERN WORLD, NO influence has had greater impact on the growth of our civilization than climate. The effect produced by the vagaries of local weather conditions has caused so many changes in the course of our history that many books would be required to record them all. It is no wonder man often bewails the fact that his life is buffeted by "the winds of chance."

In ancient times men were aware of this even without being able to look back through history. They were as often impatient with the weather as we are today, and they sought to change its un-

alterable course by using all the powers within their command. When Xerxes was waiting to cross the Hellespont in 480 B.C., he was thwarted by huge waves caused by a storm; according to legend, he ordered 10,000 slaves to lash the waves with whips to still the turbulent sea. When the waves finally subsided, he built a bridge consisting of boats across the Hellespont and took 1,000,000 men into Greece to accomplish the conquest of that country.

The caprices of weather have sometimes produced amazing coincidences which influenced the destinies of men almost as if they were the result of some higher, well-ordered design. Napoleon, who was contemptuous of lesser generals and defeated them with ease, was frequently the victim of weather during his final years. He called this adversary "General Mud" and spoke of the elements as though they were opposing forces to be reckoned with, like the armies of his enemies.

In May, 1812, Napoleon declared war upon the Russians. He left Dresden with an army of 650,000 men and, as in all his campaigns, scored quick victories.

But the losses were heavy during the march. Once upon Russian soil, the troops were enveloped by stifling heat. The recruits from the cool northern plains of Western Europe had never seen such a summer. They suffered heat prostration by the hundreds. The army moved sluggishly, mile after mile through the Russian country, unable to catch the elusive foe. On August 16th, Napoleon arrived in Smolensk. A long, hot month later he entered Moscow victoriously, but the troops were tired, lethargic. There was none of the elation of former conquests. Instead, the men were uneasy.

The Russians were different from their earlier enemies. As they retreated, they destroyed the farms and the cities they left behind, taking all the available food supplies with them. Also, and this was to become important later, cities were burned to the ground. Neither houses nor shelter were left

standing. Napoleon entered Moscow on September 15, 1812. Before the first flush of victory had faded from the troops, they were beset by troubles. Either by chance or design, a fire was started by the retreating Russians which burned for five days, destroying so much of the city that the French troops were forced to live in the desolate surrounding countryside.

The Russian Czar fled to St. Petersburg in despair. But he was counselled to wait and see what Napoleon would do before signing an armistice. Could Napoleon follow to St. Petersburg, crushing all before him? With the fierce Russian winter rapidly approaching, his troops trembled with fear at the very thought. Could he stay in Moscow and wait for the spring to continue the campaign? Not without food and shelter for his men.

For about six weeks Napoleon did nothing except sit in Moscow and fret, eyeing the signs of advancing autumn with anxiety. Finally, there was nothing left to do but to retreat. The French Army was accustomed to living off the countries they conquered. But the path of retreat lay along the desolate roads they travelled with such high hopes only a few months before.

Records show that the Russian winter of 1812 was unusually early and arrived with unprecedented cold. Cold, famine, and disease—the

Soldiers dressed in white camouflage advance against an imaginary foe during winter manoeuvres. An armed personnel carrier follows them through the snow. "General Winter" has sometimes been the "victor" in training exercises held in temperatures which often drop below −50° F.

Equipment is pounded against the beaches off the coast of France in the invasion of Normandy during World War II. Weather has always been a vital factor in warfare.

age-old enemies of the soldier—quickly took over the army. When the once-proud corps again reached Smolensk, they were only 40,000 strong. Battered by gales, shivering and demoralized, with frost-bitten limbs, they stumbled on, leaving bloody footprints in the snow. The bridges had been destroyed and the soldiers were forced to swim the ice-flecked rivers. During the month of December over 10,000 horses died each week.

Before they reached French soil, only 25,000 men remained and many of these would never fight again. It was Napoleon's first defeat, and it clearly was inflicted by General Weather, since only a small fraction of the casualties were due to enemy action. Napoleon never forgot that terrible winter, because his star fell further with each gust of the cold Russian wind. The strength of the army was broken and in April, 1813, he fled into exile on the island of Elba.

Perhaps the memory of this defeat was still upon him at Waterloo a year and a half later. In this final and most dramatic battle of his career, he was again defeated, mainly by weather.

After his return from Elba, Napoleon immediately had to prepare for battles with the armies of other Western European countries which invaded the French frontier. He decided to divide the armies aligned against him, and the showdown began in the month of June, 1815.

On the 16th, Napoleon defeated the Prussians under General Blucher at Ligny; on the 17th his army marched on the town of Waterloo where the British troops under command of the Duke of Wellington were waiting.

During the month of June, Europe is often clouded by damp seasonal fronts which leave the heavy loam soil of northeastern France and Belgium soaked with rain. The days preceding the Battle of Waterloo had produced just such a weather condition, and Napoleon fought and marched through heavy rain.

On the night of the 17th he tested the ground of the battlefield and decided to delay the attack until the earth dried sufficiently to allow a firm foundation for his heavy guns. The nearby presence of the Prussians at Ligny was a nagging worry, but he did not believe they could have reorganized their forces in time to be of any assistance to Wellington.

The warm spring sun rose on the morning of the 18th about 4:00 A.M., but Napoleon had to wait until noon before joining battle, because of the soft mud. At 6:00 P.M. he was on the verge of victory. But sometime before, the advance guard of the Prussians came over the crested hills; and shortly after 6:00 P.M., the forces which he had defeated only two days before had joined the British. In another two hours Napoleon's army was defeated and his power broken forever. The rest of his life was spent on the island of Helena where he often speculated on the fateful rain which prevented his early attack and produced his final defeat.

Early in the war year of 1943 the Japanese had begun to suffer severe setbacks among the steaming islands of the South Pacific. The Allies had been able to establish many air bases in the jungle, and planes from these bases were exacting a heavy toll from the troops and ships of Imperial Japan.

One such base had been established at Wau, 140 miles from Port Moresby on New Guinea island. Planes from this Australian base were a continuous and deadly threat to the Japanese troops on New Britain and to the ships which supplied them.

As a result, the Japanese High Command decided to reinforce the garrison at Lae only 40 miles away so that an assault could be made upon this airfield. Seven thousand soldiers were to be brought down from Rabaul, 350 miles to the northeast, to perform the job. Plans were laid carefully. The ships were loaded so that equipment could be removed from them quickly. Air support was to be supplied from the most convenient bases; however, it was realized that such protection would be limited, because much of the water traversed would be a considerable distance from operating airfields.

Even the weather was considered. Observation planes found a front just off New Guinea, and this was tracked carefully with the idea that it would provide excellent cover for the plodding ships. Thus the stage was set for the Battle of Bismarck Sea, which was to have a considerably different outcome than originally anticipated, mainly because of unexpected and unpredictable changes in the weather.

Under the command of Admiral Kimura, the convoy set sail long before dawn on the first of March. The force consisted of eight transports and seven destroyers. The ship commanders were optimistic as they steamed out of the port at Rabaul. The sky was filled with low, turbulent clouds hanging over thick rain. Under such conditions it was very unlikely that the convoy would be spotted by Allied aircraft; the weather would make co-ordinated air attacks next to impossible. Everyone knew that airmen the world over had a healthy respect for the storm clouds of the equatorial front, because they are filled with hail, violent turbulence, and severe lightning.

All through the first of March the ships nosed through the water placidly. But late in the afternoon, the equatorial front perversely shifted north out of the line of the intended track of the convoy. The rain stopped and the ceiling lifted; the color of the clouds lightened from their former dirty grey, and there was unmistakable evidence

Moderate seas permit the unloading of vehicles at a Normandy beachhead.

of a definite thinning in the overcast. The Japanese officers began to scream at the lookouts nervously enjoining them to search the skies carefully. Their uneasiness increased when just before sunset the convoy sighted a lone B-24 under the stratus clouds.

Spirits fell as the weather improved. The morning of the second dawned with hardly a cloud in the sky. By 10:00 A.M. the convoy was attacked by planes which sank one transport and damaged two others. The next day was far worse for the Japanese. By this time the convoy gleamed nakedly under the tropical sun, visible for over 25 miles. The planes of the United States Army Air Force and the Royal Australian Air Force came out in full strength. When they had finished their work of destruction, only four destroyers of the original 15 ships remained undamaged. During the night the United States Navy's torpedo boats completed the destruction, so that by morning all the damaged ships were sunk.

During World War II there were many such examples of battles won and lost by the weather. While it can be argued that the elements show no partiality and that the effect on both sides should balance out, this is not altogether true. Generally speaking, invading troops are at some disadvantage, as was shown during the campaigns of Napoleon. This is because invading armies are not accustomed to the climate of a strange country, nor do their leaders usually have the foresight to equip them with the clothing and tools necessary for operations under unfamiliar weather conditions.

However, in his constant search for perfection, modern man is making strides to equip his soldiers and sailors to fight in any sort of weather. New experiments are constantly being made to determine the tools necessary for fighting men in all parts of the world. As the science of weather progresses, man may well learn to control the weather and use it to his advantage in both war and peace. At that distant time perhaps man will change weather instead of allowing it to alter the course of his plans as he must today.

Along that historic stretch of beach which comprises the European side of the English Channel, there is no more sparsely populated and desolate sector than the 60-mile reach between Caen on the east and the Normandy Peninsula to the west. The tides are strong, and they have pushed up long slopes of damp sand below the sea wall. The hard ground above is divided into pastures which are centuries old and separated by earth walls known as hedgerows. These are overgrown with thick tangled bushes and lined by drainage ditches which create perfect natural trenches.

American troops debark under fire from German artillery during the early stages of the D-Day invasion. Amphibious operations such as these are at the mercy of the weather.

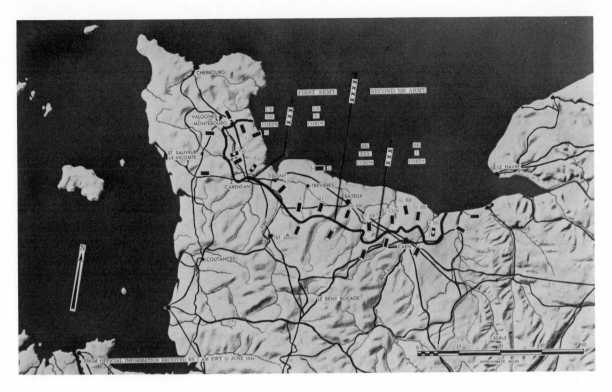

This is a map of the first phase of the Normandy invasion.

At first glance it would seem that there are many places along the coast which would provide a more logical point of entry for an amphibious assault. However, when the Allied generals began to go over their maps in the autumn of 1943, they studied this section carefully. It nestles almost baylike between the Peninsula and the rocky protuberances of the Pas de Calais area, and the smoothing effect of the Carentan Estuary eliminates much of the nasty chopping sea for which the English Channel is famous. Also, the fact that the area is sheltered from the prevailing westerly winds by the Normandy Peninsula did not escape the military planners. As a result of these considerations, it was decided to launch Operation Overlord between Caen and Carentan, and the first decision of the greatest military operation in modern times was made.

The invasion of Europe was first scheduled to begin during the propitious period of the May moon in 1944. Actually, due to the relationship between tides and morning twilight, the time of the initial assault was limited to six days of each month. Twice each day the beaches of Normandy are flooded with a tremendous tide which rises 19 feet from low to high water. Landing at low tide meant that Allied troops would lie on the half-mile of flat, sandy beach between the low water and the sea wall and be exposed to enemy fire. The ideal condition for landing thus seemed to be a dawn high tide, so that they could gain the protection of the bank as early as possible. This would prevent disasters like that of Tarawa in the Pacific campaign.

However, the enemy also appreciated this fact and had strung the approaches with mines, barbed wire and other obstacles located halfway between low and high tide. These obstructions had to be blasted away by the army demolition teams. Since the tide rose at a rate of one foot every 15 minutes, and the engineers estimated it would take 30 minutes to clear the water, it was decided to launch the attack just as the rising tide reached the obstacle line.

Allied weathermen soon dissuaded the generals from launching the attack in May. The statistics which had been gathered carefully over many years showed conclusively that May was a month of high winds and heavy rains. Summer often comes late in Northern Europe, and spring is likely to be turbulent. In order to make the best use of landing craft and air coverage, good weather

Some of the damage caused by the storm of June 19, 1944, at Omaha Beach, Normandy. Fortunately the Allied beachhead was firmly established before this storm struck.

was necessary. Also, the Russian thaw normally begins in earnest about the middle of May; once the frozen steppes began to melt, it would be possible to launch an offensive on the eastern front which would fully occupy the German troops in that area, so that they could not be diverted to defeat the invasion attempt before it gained a foothold.

It soon became apparent that the period from June 5th to June 9th offered the most advantages. Just the right amount of daylight would be provided to allow the demolition teams to do their dangerous job in the filling tide after the beaches had been approached under cover of darkness. Accordingly, D Day was set for June 5th.

Nothing was left to chance. More than a million men were stationed in England, training for the amphibious assault, and many operation orders were written totalling millions of words. Several of these contained more words than *Forever Amber*, the best-selling historical novel at that time. The weather observers attached to General Eisenhower's staff worked at top speed. They compared the current weather conditions all over the globe with those of past years, seeking to establish the trend from similar weather patterns. As D Day approached, they became increasingly optimistic. The snows were melting normally from the lower mountains of Canada; the ice began to break in the northern rivers on schedule. Indications from all over the world pointed to a mild European spring.

Then almost as if to prove that man's best plans were still at the mercy of the elements, the weather turned bad. A low-pressure area drifted slowly but inexorably from the west across Plymouth and Brest, bringing low-stratus clouds that spread thick billowing fingers over the invasion area. The Channel waves swelled into turbulent, white-tufted crests. On the afternoon of Saturday, June 3rd, the weather report read as follows: "Mist from 4 to 7 June with low clouds and reduced visibility in the mornings. Rain. Winds not to exceed 20 to 25 miles per hour. Choppy water in the Channel with five-foot breakers. A four-foot surf on the beaches."

The hopes of the invasion force fell. The troops already briefed were excommunicated from the world on their invasion craft. Any delay meant that they must be kept aboard so there could be no possible leakage of this, the most closely guarded secret of the war. The operation was so large and complex that some ships were already on their way from the northern ports; many wheels had already begun to turn in anticipation of the target date of June 5th. But to proceed in foul weather would be an invitation to the worst disaster of the war. The beaches would be tricky on landing, air support for the troops would be impossible under the thick low clouds, and no spotting planes could be used to direct the fire of naval guns which were to knock out the heavy pillboxes and fortifications on the invasion coast.

Thus General Eisenhower was faced with one

of the most fateful decisions of all time. A mistake in judgment could produce incalculable disaster and prolong the war indefinitely. After studying the problem and conferring with his weathermen, two words flashed from the powerful radio station at his command headquarters: HORNPIPE BOWSPRIT. They meant that the invasion was to be delayed one day.

Slowly the tense hours passed. The weather held monotonously with drizzle falling softly from the thick grey clouds. Gusty 25-mile-per-hour winds whipped the Channel seas.

The weathermen on General Eisenhower's staff spent a sleepless night on the fourth of June. If the storm lasted for three more days, it would mean that the invasion could not be launched for two weeks, since it would be that long before there was another high tide at daybreak. If the weather was again unsatisfactory, there could be no invasion until July, and the summer would then be almost half gone. History was full of grim reminders recording the disasters arising out of campaigns launched too near the approach of winter. The weathermen knew that few supplies could be landed on the beaches during the autumn. This meant that it was imperative that a Channel port be captured before the first of September.

Tensely the meteorologists studied the teletype machines which brought them weather information gathered all around the world. Each new pressure was quickly plotted on their maps; each change in temperature and wind shift was watched eagerly for its effects on the weather equation.

The troops turned in on the night of the fourth with full expectations that they would receive another postponement the next day. Indeed, the morning of June 5th brought no improvement in the weather. The same grey stratus clouds were overhead, and through the jetties the waiting soldiers could see the whitecaps on the wind-tossed breakers.

But the weathermen had detected a possible break. The evidence was tantalizingly meagre but nevertheless unmistakable on the maps. After rechecking the figures, they came up with a forecast that was immediately sent to Eisenhower: "The weather will clear during the afternoon. The winds will lessen and the cloud ceiling will definitely rise over the invasion coast. This condition should hold through the morning of June 6th. After that the clouds will close in again and the winds will probably increase."

General Eisenhower squinted at the stormy clouds outside his headquarters for a few long moments. Then, reluctantly, he made his decision. The kickoff for Operation Overlord was definitely

These troops under General Eisenhower had their faces blackened because they were paratroopers who would fight under cover of darkness during the Normandy invasion.

A distant thermonuclear explosion raises its deadly cloud far above the Pacific. Atomic clouds rise to greater distances and are more turbulent than the largest thunderclouds. Their shape is somewhat similar to that of the cumulo-nimbus.

set for dawn on June 6th. Long afterwards, Norman Hagen, one of the expert meteorologists present at the time, told General Eisenhower that his decision was the most courageous ever made in wartime having to do with the weather.

The weather on D Day did not turn out to be exactly what the weathermen would have ordered. A flight of heavy bombers sent over to reduce fortifications in the beach area overshot their target by three miles due to low clouds, and their bombs exploded harmlessly in the hedgerows beyond. Many a soldier was seasick that morning as his landing craft tossed in the heavy swells off the beach. But the weather was good enough to permit the landing of the equivalent of 200 trainloads of troops during the first day. Also, the high seas cluttered the radar screens and the poor visibility obscured the Channel, so that the passage of the invasion ships went undiscovered until their arrival off the beaches.

In retrospect, General Eisenhower's decision became even more sound. On June 18th, during the next high tide, a vicious, unusually violent summer storm, which would have precluded all possibility of the landings, struck the invasion area. During this storm more landing craft were lost in the Channel than on D Day itself.

During April, 1945, a conference was held in the Pentagon in Washington. It was a small group as conferences go, but one of the most important of the war. Those present spent most of their time leaning over weather maps and listening to the words of a white-haired old man from Norway who spoke broken English. The Norwegian was an expert on air masses, and the conference had been called to usher in a new era. These men had gathered together to decide when and where they would drop the first atomic bomb.

They decided on three possible targets: Hiroshima, Kokura, and Nagasaki. The question of the time was a little more difficult. There were no bombs to waste, and once the plane left for the target there could be no turning back. The timing and the execution of the operation had to be letter-perfect; so did the weather.

Finally, after an intensive study of his maps, charts, and statistics, the old man gave them his decision. There would be a period of three days beginning August 6th when the weather conditions over Japan would be just right for the drop.

Those who were to drop the bomb went from the Pentagon to prepare for the event. General Curtis LeMay, Commander of the Western Pacific Strategic Air Force, would make the final decision as to target and time. Every day after the first of August weather reports were gathered from China, Russia and the Philippines. At 1:00 P.M. each afternoon General LeMay received a complete briefing on the weather. A half-hour later he made his daily decision on whether or not to send the bomb.

For the first four days the decision was no. There was a weak but persistent summer cold front lying over the Japanese Islands. Finally on the afternoon of the fifth, the front looked as though it were moving out and General LeMay decided on the next morning. Long before the bomb-carrying B-29 arrived over the target area, the crew received reports from three weather planes, which had been sent out ahead of time to observe conditions at the three cities. The reports showed that Hiroshima had the best weather, and the decision on where to deliver the bomb was made then.

On the morning of August 6th, as the atom-bomb plane flew in, the air over Japan was partially filled with large tufted cumulus clouds; as chance would have it, there was a large hole in the clouds over Hiroshima. Minutes later this hole was filled by the famous mushrooming cloud of the bomb, and those in the plane were the first to realize that our world would never be quite the same again. Because of the accuracy of modern weather forecasting, the bomb was delivered within 15 seconds of the time planned six months before.

Three days later a second bomb was dropped, this time on Nagasaki. This time the weather was not so co-operative. The primary target was Kokura because the weather was best there. However, for some reason it was obscured by smoke. After three passes the bombing plane went on to Nagasaki where the weather was much worse. Ninety per cent of the bombing run had to be made by radar. But in the last moments the target could be seen beneath the clouds.

During the autumn of 1944 objects were reported in the air over the northwestern United States by the inhabitants of that region. These were variously described as huge balls of fire about the size of the moon and as parachute-like devices floating dreamily over the Oregon and Washington hills.

This is a cross-section of the famous mushroom cloud formed by a nuclear explosion. Such clouds reach more than 25 miles into the stratosphere and extend 50 miles on either side of the detonation point.

STRATOSPHERE

100 MILES

25 MILES

Military men and scientists listened to the stories with interest. There were many possibilities: meteors, weather-observation balloons, and the redoubtable flying saucers immediately came to mind. But one other idea was worth considering: they might be the result of some unknown secret weapon unleashed by the Japanese. About the same time, the strategic bombing planes striking the Japanese cities reported another peculiar phenomenon. On the way to their targets, they encountered huge balloons rising to tremendous heights.

Shortly after these strange occurrences, an unusually large number of fires began breaking out in the Pacific Northwest. Also, bits of rice paper were found on the streets of Los Angeles, and unexplainable explosions were heard near some of the West Coast towns and cities.

A meeting of weathermen and other scientists ascertained the facts and came up with the right answer. The Japanese were launching huge balloons against the United States which contained explosives, incendiaries, and perhaps even germs.

The idea of possible biological warfare was enough to galvanize even the most confirmed skeptics into action. Warnings were published to all civilians telling them not to touch strange objects. Teams were formed and sent out to capture some of these balloons so that they could be examined. Finally, several were captured intact.

The principle of operation was amazingly simple. As mentioned in an earlier chapter, the earth's rotation causes a basic west-to-east circulation of the atmosphere. Balloons launched in Japan were carried swiftly eastwards at high altitude by the swiftly flowing air. Their altitude was stabilized at about 30,000 feet by means of an air-pressure device which released sand ballast when they began to sink.

By the time the balloons reached the coast of the United States all the sand had been dropped in order to make up for the loss of hydrogen which leaked out slowly through the bag. Then they began dropping more deadly cargo—bombs and incendiaries. The Japanese had not begun trying germs before the war ended.

Since the gases which they contained were cooler and therefore more dense at night, the balloons became heavier relative to the atmosphere during the hours of darkness. It was then that they usually descended.

By the time the war ended, it was estimated that nearly 1,000 balloons had been dropped on the United States. Some of them penetrated as far

A nuclear cloud rises over the Arizona desert. The deadly fallout particles are carried into the upper atmosphere by the force of the explosion.

east as Detroit, while others flew north into Canada and Alaska. Without the comparatively recent knowledge of the general atmospheric flow pattern this type of warfare would have been impossible.

The atmosphere is able to yield information of considerable importance about other countries. This fact received considerable attention when President Truman announced, in October, 1951, that the Russians had exploded an atomic bomb. By far, the least dangerous method of obtaining information of Russian atomic activities is to analyze the contents of the current of atmosphere.

The process by which this is done has been described recently in several scientific publications. Two physicists, Norman Holter and W. R. Glasscock of Helena, Montana, collected rain water from stratus clouds over the city and filtered it through cotton. During 1951 and 1952 they found that some of this filter cotton was contaminated with radioactive material. Tests indicated that the contaminating substance was identical to the radioactive particles found in clouds produced by atomic explosions. Such clouds formed by Russian tests have been deflected over the United States countryside by jet streams and the natural circulation of the atmosphere. Thus, Western Countries can detect atomic explosions in Russia despite the blanket of secrecy imposed by the Iron Curtain.

In the short span of recorded history, the effect of climate upon civilization has been of tremendous importance. Other weather influences, undoubtedly even more vital, accompanied the dawn of this world. It is safe to predict that the future will produce many more changes based on the ever-changing climate. Although man has learned to use many of the elements on his earth, he must still open many doors and discover many hidden natural laws before he will be able to control the weather of his globe.

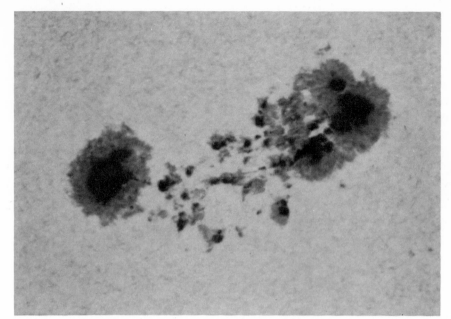

A close-up of sunspot activity. These spots are each much larger than the earth and may last for several days. They produce many electrical disturbances on the earth's surface.

13. The Electric Blanket

BEYOND THE GRASP OF OUR SENSES LIES ANOTHER world, hidden from our gaze and intangible to our touch, but nonetheless real. This is the world of electricity. It is like the movement of time and the deep currents of the sea, unseen and unheard. Yet we can measure the electrical elements and we know the laws of its timeless flow.

We also have come to realize that the incredible atmosphere is more than a sea of gases, more than a pattern of wind and storm. In every layer of our atmospheric blanket, electrical currents weave their intricate tapestry so that the envelope of air has become a gigantic electric field and a storehouse of power far beyond the total capacity of all the world's dams.

The full significance of this amazing property of our atmosphere has been realized only during the last few years. But men have always been awed by the brilliant lightning patterns of the vertical storm clouds and the spectacular dances performed by the northern lights. In much the same fashion, the auroras and the eerie glow of St. Elmo's fire puzzled them for many ages. But it remained for the development of radio and radar to provide the first basic clues which led to an understanding of the electrical atmosphere.

At first, man thought he had created electricity. But further investigation has forced him to accept a much more humble role. He merely discovered it, and rather belatedly too, since he had been face-to-face with all the evidence of its existence from the beginning of time. But once he became aware of the electronic world, he probed diligently at its secrets and learned to harness the electrical elements to do his bidding. In the process he uncovered many mysteries of the sea of air which puzzled him through the long unenlightened centuries.

To understand the relationship between atmosphere and electricity, it is helpful to visualize the earth and its surrounding gases as a gigantic dynamo of vast circumference and intricate design. The upper atmosphere can be regarded as the rotor or whirling envelope, while the earth provides the magnetic field. As in our conventional generator, it is the interaction of the one upon the other which causes the electrical flow.

Dr. Sydney Chapman of the University of Iowa has developed a theory which explains many of the unknown elements in the vast electrical field around the earth. He believes that the great storms on the sun which we see as sunspots emit large quantities of electrified matter. This is mainly in the form of ionized hydrogen—hydrogen atoms which have lost some of their electrons. These hydrogen ions and an approximately equal number of negatively charged electrons are captured by the earth's magnetic field and whirled like tiny moons in an electrified ring about 6,000 to 11,000 miles above our sphere.

The positive ions are much heavier than the electrons, and for this reason they must travel faster in their orbits around the earth. The great space ring thus becomes a powerful current of positive electricity flowing around the earth. Periodically, the ring dips down and curves into the lower atmosphere to cause many strange and weird electrical phenomena.

Dr. Chapman's theory is interesting not only because it explains the creation of the aurora but also because it may clarify another electrical enigma. It has been known for some time that mysterious measurable electrical currents flow in the earth's crust, similar to those which exist at high altitude. We now believe that this current is induced by a flow of electricity in the air-borne electrical ring. Dr. Chapman's electrified ring makes it appear as though nature has preceded man in another of his most prized inventions, the electric motor.

The bombardment of the earth by solar radiation is responsible for one of the great layers of the atmosphere, the ionosphere. Located directly above the blanket of ozone, about 100 miles above our heads, this region is characterized by the presence of many diverse electrical currents which are created when the ultraviolet radiation from the sun is absorbed by the earth's rarefied gases. The ionosphere is not uniform throughout but contains several concentrated electrical layers which have been designated by the letters of the alphabet. Each layer is caused when the atoms of a specific gas become ionized. The D layer, for example, consists mainly of ionized molecular oxygen. These great electrical circuits of the atmosphere were first predicted by the English scientist, Oliver Heaviside, and are now called Heaviside layers.

The D layer is particularly opaque to low-frequency radio waves. Like a giant, hollow mirror, it reflects radio transmissions back from the upper atmosphere to receiving stations on the

Spectrum

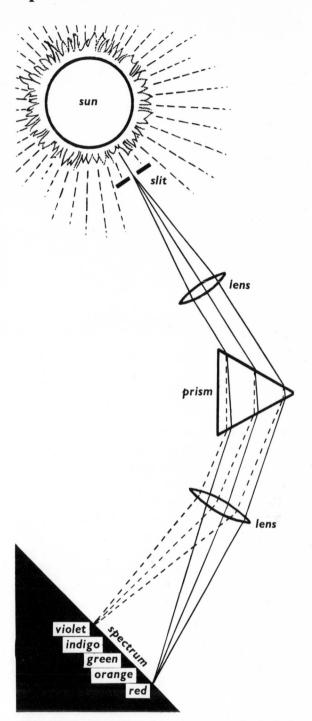

This diagram shows how the sun's spectrum is obtained. Analysis of this spectrum has taught us a great deal about the chemical composition of the sun.

earth, thousands of miles away from the transmitter. If it were not for the D layer, radio transmission would not be effective over a few hundred miles.

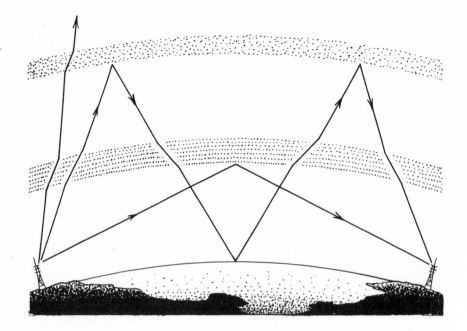

Radio waves are reflected by the layers of the atmosphere so that they can be heard at great distances. Unfortunately, such transmissions are not very reliable.

Sometimes, however, the D layer cannot be trusted to relay our radio signals. During periods when there is intense sunspot activity, the D layer becomes very intense. For reasons which are not entirely clear, it then acts as a trap to absorb the radio waves it formerly reflected. At such times, radio fade-outs plague us and service may be totally disrupted. A more common annoyance is the fading caused by momentary shifts in the position of the electronic mirror. These cause erratic radio reception. At night the bombardment of the sun is deflected from the D layer by the earth, causing a reduction in its strength. Less transmitted energy is absorbed and the mirrors work their best for us. Long-wave transmissions are excellent in the earth's shadow.

The most spectacular and dangerous electrical phenomenon created in our atmosphere is lightning. The mighty flash and reverberating sound of the electrical discharge have struck fear in the hearts of men throughout the ages. Generally, lightning is born in cumulus clouds, which are characterized by their high vertical development and relatively small surface area. A mature thunderstorm cloud may extend up from a lower level of 2,000 feet to 25,000 feet. It will contain over 1,000,000 tons of water mist and almost 1,000,000 volts of potential electrical energy. One bolt of lightning from such a cloud may discharge electrical power in the amount of 50,000 kilowatt hours. This is enough electricity to light a medium-sized city for three hours.

Lightning almost invariably accompanies a torrential downpour of rain. The falling droplets are mixed by the turbulent air and rubbed against each other until many of them are broken up into water mist. This rubbing causes an effect similar to that produced when a comb is drawn across the back of a cat. A charge of static electricity is produced. The smaller particles of water mist become negatively charged and are carried skyward by ascending, charged droplets, remain in the lower regions of the atmosphere, or fall to the ground as rain. The steady accumulation of negatively charged particles in the upper atmosphere and positively charged droplets at the surface cause a large electrical difference in charge.

When the electrical potential becomes strong enough, it suddenly discharges its energy by means of a bolt of lightning. The brilliant stroke of static electricity may traverse six miles from sky to earth, or from cloud to cloud, in a fraction of a second. The thunderclap caused by the rapid expansion of air may be heard for 15 or 20 miles.

For centuries the lightning bolt was man's main contact with the static electrical fields in the atmosphere. Then we learned to fly. Early pilots were terrified when they first observed an eerie bluish light or corona flickering around their propellers as they flew through areas of rain or snowfall. With the advent of metal aircraft this phenomenon became more common. It is called *St. Elmo's fire* and has been identified as a "junior partner" of lightning. As rain or snow strike the metal parts of the aircraft, they carry away some of the surface electrons. When the aircraft passes through suitably charged clouds, it discharges its unwelcome electrical passengers in the form of minute electrical charges or St. Elmo's fire.

This static electrical life exists only in the lower regions of the atmosphere near the surface and within the weather zone. The currents in the upper layers are infinitely stronger and more diverse; as yet we have been unable to measure them. For the most part, they are invisible, but occasionally we receive a manifestation of them in the form of the *aurora borealis*, a spectacle which has thrilled and fascinated man since the beginning of time.

The aurora borealis owes its name to the Greek goddess of dawn, Aurora, who was purported to rise over the sea, drawn by the celestial horses, Lampus and Phaethon, and who raised the curtain of night with fire-draped arms. The early Latin poets described her as the wife of Titan, the sun god, and said that she preceded him in his endless race around the world, strewing rosy flowers in his path.

The thin, ghostlike streamers of the aurora borealis streak across the heavens during spring and autumn evenings, causing man to lift up his eyes in awe. Of all the spectacles in the atmospheric bag of fireworks, none has a greater variety of color and form. Often the auroras unfurl in dazzling sheets of light similar to the lower edge of a wind-blown flag. Sometimes they hang almost still in the night. At other times they spread upward in pulsing brilliance, radiating in an arc which fills half the sky. Occasionally they appear as though huge, dancing searchlight beams in the upper middle latitudes near both Poles; for this reason they are called *northern lights*.

The auroral hues range the spectrum. The stronger colors are most often an odd shade between yellow and green. Red, grey, violet, and blue shades may be seen sometimes, and the cur-

tain or flag-type of auroral display will often appear as pale chartreuse, fading from a brilliant red along its lower border. The auroral light seems to be similar to that appearing in the conventional neon tube. The shades coincide with those produced by the electrification of certain ionized gases such as atomic oxygen and nitrogen, which are known to exist in the upper atmosphere. Electrification of oxygen produces yellow, red, and green; nitrogen glows orange, blue-green, blue-violet, and a deep violet-grey shade. The operation of a conventional neon tube requires a heavy charge of electricity to pass through a dense concentration of such gases. Just how this process occurs at heights of 600 miles above the earth's surface is a puzzling mystery, but it is known to be intimately related to the sky-earth dynamo discussed earlier.

The creating impulse for the auroras appears to be the sun. Clues suggesting this were first noticed when scientists found there was a distinct relationship between the appearance of the auroras and the seasons. The greatest numbers of auroral banners are seen at the start of the spring and autumn; the fewest when winter and summer begin. Astronomers then found that the auroral displays rise from their lowest ebb to their greatest frequency in about 26 days, a figure matched almost exactly by the rotational period of the sun. The evidence is being gathered gradually. So far, it indicates that the auroras are related to the sun and more particularly to the great solar storms we call *sunspots*.

The solar rays which create our weather and warm our planet are also the source of the mysterious electrical patterns that race through our sea of air. The great earth-and-atmosphere generator receives its impulses from the same energy machine. When the stars appear on some clear future evening, a scientist may throw a switch which will draw current from this gigantic dynamo to light the world. If this day should come, man will have tapped the endless cosmic resources outside his sphere. He will no longer need to fret over the depletion of the natural riches and the fuel on this globe, and the forces which bind our whirling universe will provide the energy to sustain him for as long as his world exists.

Time and weather are the great architects of earth.

14. Aerial Treasure House

THE ANCIENT PHYSICIANS BELIEVED THAT LIVING things contained a magic elixir which vitally charged their bodies with the mysterious breath of life. But careful analysis of living cells has convinced latter-day scientists that there is no chemical with such remarkable properties. As a matter of fact, they are now convinced that the cells of plants, animals and human beings are formed of the prosaic, abundant chemical elements; those most plentifully found in the atmosphere.

If all the constituents of the air around us were broken down into their component elements, we would find they bear a remarkable relationship to the chemistry of living things. The atmosphere contains nitrogen, oxygen, carbon, and hydrogen in either combined or uncombined form. Analysis of life-substances shows that the great majority of living cells are also made up of these four atoms. Carbohydrates and fats consist almost solely of carbon, hydrogen and oxygen; proteins are built of these three plus nitrogen. While it is true that other substances are found in living cells, the four main atmospheric elements are by far the most abundant.

Scientists know that the atmosphere has gone through many stages of evolutionary development and change. During the formative stages of the first living cells, its composition is believed to have been methane, ammonia, water, and hydrogen. Basically, the elements which compose these gases remain in our atmosphere today; the present elements, carbon, oxygen, and nitrogen, were then merely combined into different molecules. The changes and mutations in the atmosphere have been caused by the development of life, the temperature variations in the earth's crust, and the natural decomposition of the original gases through the ages. The first minute supply of oxygen probably came as a result of lightning discharges in the early thunderstorms, which decomposed the vitriolic atmosphere and released free oxygen to combine with other elements.

The first traces of oxygen led to the development of early plants such as the green translucent algae, Corycia, which quickly covered the embryo seas. These algae in turn manufactured more oxygen from the carbon dioxide in the air, and more complex plants gradually evolved through the long dark centuries. Shortly, as time is measured in the growth of planets, the oxygen-consuming creatures began to appear and the carbon dioxide—oxygen cycle was born.

The carbon dioxide—oxygen cycle is the precise, never-failing process by which the plants, the animals and the atmosphere maintain a mutual partnership for self-support. Oxygen from the air is inhaled by all members of the animal kingdom, and carbon dioxide is exhaled. The reverse is true of plants. This is a simple but vital cycle which revitalizes the atmosphere for both plants and animals. Interrupt the cycle or change its balance, and life on earth as we know it would soon die.

The dwellers of the sea are not exempt from this gigantic chemical Ferris wheel. The great oceans of the earth absorb both oxygen and carbon dioxide in large quantities; the teeming life within them feasts on these products. The oceans have captured carbon dioxide in such quantities that they now hold 50 times as much as the atmosphere.

The conversion of carbon dioxide into carbon and oxygen is not difficult by chemical standards; any skilled chemist can perform such a transformation with ease. The creation of carbon dioxide is even more simple. It is one of the products of combustion, and one need only start a fire to manufacture huge quantities of the element.

Despite the simplicity of these experiments in the laboratory, man has not been able to discover how living creatures can accomplish such processes within their own bodies. In a rather startling departure from her usual methods, nature has chosen much more difficult processes to accomplish the same work. It is known that two extremely complex molecules are intimately tied into the cycle. They are chlorophyll and haemoglobin.

Chlorophyll is the agent which causes the green hue that spreads across our lawns in the spring as the plants begin to grow. It extracts the carbon dioxide from the air and, with the aid of solar radiation and moisture, transforms this gas into stringy cellulose or plant fibre. Oxygen is released in the process, and this unique action is called photosynthesis. We understand what goes in and what comes out; we know the in-between products. But although the process goes on about us every day, we know practically nothing of how it is accomplished.

The oxygen rejected by the chlorophyll molecules is breathed into the lungs of animals, and haemoglobin takes over. This element, found in the blood of almost all animals, transports the oxygen to the capillary veins in the muscles, where it can be burned along with carbon in the energy-making process. Haemoglobin then picks up the carbon dioxide which results from this burning and returns it to the lungs, where it is breathed out as waste gas. Again, we understand the results of the process, but we do not know how it is done. Haemoglobin appears to act in much the same manner as our dairyman who brings us milk every morning and takes away our empty bottles.

Another unusual factor in this amazing life cycle is that the haemoglobin in the blood and the chlorophyll in the plants are very similar in their chemical structure. Both are complex compounds having a molecule of metal tied to their middles. Chlorophyll contains the element magnesium, while haemoglobin has iron in its nucleus.

Nature apparently knows a good molecule when she sees one. Chemical structures similar to haemoglobin and chlorophyll are found in many creatures of the sea, such as the king crab and the octopus. These have similar proteins flowing in their vital fluids, with a molecule of copper acting as their key to existence.

As oxygen and carbon dioxide are replenished in the air, nitrogen must be added continuously to maintain the tight balance of atmospheric elements. For this reason, nature has provided our world with a nitrogen cycle to replace the gas which is lost to plants, animals, and (by the process of absorption) the earth's crust.

Some types of soil bacteria take nitrogen directly from the air and convert it into many useful compounds used as food by plants and animals. During electrical storms nitrogen and oxygen are often combined into nitric or nitrous acid by electrical discharge. Certain plants known as legumes, such as clover, absorb nitrogen directly from the air. This nitrogen is ultimately transferred to the earth by the bacteria which feed on the plants and by the decay of the legumes.

Nitrogen is returned to the atmosphere in the form of ammonia from the excretions of animals. The decaying process of many plants releases free nitrogen and nitrous oxide, which become pure nitrogen and oxygen.

Yet another great chemical cycle wheels along on its endless route over our heads. This is the unique blending of hydrogen and oxygen which we call water. Unlike its partners in the cycle, carbon dioxide and nitrogen, water can be seen and tasted. It is so closely tied to the human environment that man immediately becomes conscious of its lack. It is the lubricant which greases the efficient machinery of the life processes on our earth. If its distribution were interrupted, the mechanism would grind to a sudden disastrous halt; once deprived of the solvent power of water and its ability to transfer food and heat, neither plants nor animals could live on this globe. Even if only the water mist were to be suddenly swept from our atmosphere, we could not exist, for this would allow the precious trapped heat from the sun to escape, and our planet would be chilled to sub-polar cold.

With all the evidence before him, man failed to understand until recent centuries the wheel of water rotating from earth to sky and back again. This was not through lack of study, because the source of water in the rivers and lakes puzzled men in ancient times. Aristotle believed that rainfall, together with water emerging from the deep bowels of the earth, united to form the rivers. Plato thought that ocean water flowed through subterranean channels underneath the continents to bubble forth as springs which replenished the rivers. Centuries later Kepler and Descartes subscribed to a modified form of Plato's theory. It remained for the genius of Leonardo da Vinci to suggest that river water was caused by the runoff of rainfall over the earth. Two centuries later three French scientists proved conclusively that the return of water to the land masses was the result of the atmosphere's water-carrying capacity.

Today we understand the functioning of the hydrological cycle better than any other. Millions of tons of moisture are siphoned into the atmosphere each day by the process of evaporation. The giant air masses carry this water over the land and deposit it as rainfall, which seeps through the earth, forming rivers, which flow back once more to the oceans. The evaporation process aerates and purifies the precious water so that living things can use it. About three parts in a thousand of the total water on the earth are continually involved in this moisture transfer—enough to blanket the United States under a seven-foot layer. Yet its burden is carried effortlessly by the mothering atmosphere.

The three great chemical cycles of carbon—oxygen, nitrogen, and water, have created the symbiotic partnership by which mankind and the other life forms live with the atmosphere. As individuals we scarcely perceive this partnership. The haemoglobin in our lungs functions automatically to refresh the atmosphere, and our food habits regularly supply us with the chemicals and energy to sustain life.

Only by the vigorous exercise of our conscious senses are we acutely aware of environment. The atmosphere is mainly significant to us because of the climate it creates, and rarely do we like that climate: it is either too hot or too cold, too wet or too dry. But, despite our complaints, we are superbly adjusted to the average climatic conditions of our world. It is only the extreme variations which really hurt us.

The average air temperature on the earth's surface illustrates this remarkable adjustment. Weathermen have calculated with considerable accuracy the average mean temperature for the entire world; this works out to be 64°. Independently, medical scientists have estimated the temperature which appears to be best for health and work. The ideal temperature for the human organism turns out to be exactly the same.

Thus, in a temperature sense, man resembles a perfectly designed machine. He operates with best efficiency at the condition most likely to be encountered in his environment, but he is still able to accommodate the variations which he is apt to encounter. In order to do this, he is equipped with a built-in air-conditioning unit, which under normal conditions maintains a constant body heat of 98.6°, regardless of the outside air temperature.

Erosion of the mountains by the rain and snow over many centuries has produced the jagged peaks we see today.

His temperature is controlled by a small organ at the base of his brain which is called the *hypothalamus*. It is the thermostat which turns up his furnace in the winter cold and starts his cooling mechanism during the summer. By means of an exquisitely delicate and complicated nervous system, temperature readings are taken from the blood, skin, and liver. These are relayed to the hypothalamus. When variations in body temperature occur, the thermostat sets into motion the corrective processes of the human air-conditioning system.

The internal mechanism of the body provides several methods of adjustment for heat and cold. When the outside air temperature goes up, the hypothalamus directs the surface blood vessels to dilate. More blood is shunted to the skin, where it is cooled. In this case the skin acts like the radiator of a car, and the blood vessels become the cooling jacket of water. As the veins and arteries expand, the body manufactures more blood; for this reason, we actually contain more blood in summer than we do in winter. Additional body heat can be dissipated into the atmosphere by the evaporation of perspiration, which is a cooling process. This evaporation is retarded if the atmosphere already has a high moisture content, and explains why we are so uncomfortable on muggy days, when the humidity may be higher than the air temperature.

The opposite effect occurs when the weather gets colder. Blood vessels constrict, and the blood supply grows less. Our skin glands dry up, and, instead of perspiring, we shiver. This shivering, like any other body exercise, releases energy stored in our body fat and thus helps to maintain our precious body heat.

Both the heating and cooling processes of the body require the expenditure of considerable physical effort; it is not surprising, therefore, that we catch cold easily in the autumn and spring. During these seasons the human air-conditioning unit is overworked by the changing climate. Under a really hot summer sky, the body must work hard to maintain its normal temperature. This explains why we are lazy and feel distress: it takes all our energy to avoid becoming overheated.

When the body is invaded by destructive bacteria, the function of the hypothalamus alters in some manner still unknown to us. Our bodies no longer react to temperature changes in the normal way, and we begin to run a fever. The extra heat developed is usefully employed in combating the microbes and serves to warn us that we are sick. Occasionally, even in the absence of illness, the body thermostat itself fails to perform properly, and we become very uncomfortable. On a hot summer day, when we should be damp with perspiration, our skin remains dry. When this happens, we have no energy, and our hearts pound in the effort to maintain body temperature by the circulation process alone. We develop a fever, as though we have been subject to bacterial invasion, and we become sick.

The efficiency of the human air-conditioning

This picture was taken two minutes after the detonation of a nuclear explosion showing the development of its cloud. Nuclear pollution is a growing threat to our atmosphere.

equipment is far superior to any man-made device. Dr. Craig Taylor of the University of California once conducted a series of experiments to determine the ability of the human body to withstand heat. He constructed an oven large enough to hold his body and then literally cooked himself in it. After a little practice he was able to withstand a temperature of 250° for almost 15 minutes. Perhaps this experiment helps to demonstrate why man, though physically puny, has achieved world domination over much stronger but less adaptable beings.

When man, who is designed to live healthfully at 64°, is subjected to different climates, his well-being is affected in many subtle ways. During recent years scientists have made studies to determine the most healthful areas of the world. This research has brought forth some very interesting and occasionally puzzling facts. Cancer, diabetes, and heart disease—terrible killers in the temperate zones—are quite rare in the tropics. Conversely, infections such as blood poisoning and respiratory fevers flourish in the southland. It appears that continuous hot weather reduces the energy level of the human body to an extent where it is difficult to ward off bacterial invasion. This same low energy level, however, apparently guards against so-called degenerative diseases such as cancer.

Aside from physical health, man's emotional outlook is keyed to his local climatic conditions. Perhaps we can best understand how dependent we are on climate for our well-being when we realize that even our laws have been influenced by it. In Italy, for example, crimes of passion and violence are not punished as severely during those months when the fierce, hot sirocco winds blow in from the deserts of North Africa. Whole towns are said to have become sirocco-crazed, their people driven temporarily insane by these maddening winds. In Spain there is a proverb: "Ask no boon during the Solano." The Solano season is a period of strong, hot winds, which shortens tempers and creates aggressiveness because the body's physical tolerance has already been exceeded. In New York City the temperature curve has been compared with that denoting the frequency of crimes. The two curves have been found to be almost identical. As the temperature goes up, so does crime. However, when it gets very hot—over 100°—there are few cases of assault and battery. Apparently, no one has the energy to fight.

Climate shows its effect on humans in the most surprising ways. Of the persons listed in *Who's Who in America*, more have birthdays in January and February than during any other months of the year. The majority born in these months far exceeds the number which could be laid to chance alone. Professor Ellsworth Huntington of Yale University has studied the effect of birthdates on longevity and has discovered that, on the average, people born in March live almost four years longer than those born in July. They are also stronger, hardier, and more intelligent.

Teachers have long known that students achieve their lowest marks and do their poorest work while attending summer school; conversely, they do their best work in the spring and autumn. Statistics prove that more persons taking civil-service examinations pass in springtime than at any other time.

Human beings are not the only ones who do well when the climate is cool and invigorating, for animals react in the same manner. Dr. Clarence Mills conducted some experiments with rats which demonstrated this conclusively. Three groups of rats were given the problem of finding the right passageway through a maze in order to get a piece of cheese. The temperature of the room in which the rats were placed differed with each group. The first group of rats worked their way through the maze in an average of 12 attempts when the room temperature was 65°. The second group required 28 tries when the temperature was raised to 75°. Working at 90°, the rats in a third group took 48 runs each, and some gave up altogether. It was too hot even to go after a piece of cheese.

In support of his theory of the effect of climate upon men and animals, Dr. Mills found that beef cattle in the State of Iowa reached a weight of 1,000 pounds within 12 months after birth. Steers raised in Louisiana take three years to gain the same weight. Those in Panama require five.

Despite the wide variety of weather conditions existing on our globe, all of us have a basic physical construction, and the particular climate in which we live does not cause any major differences in the development of our bodies. However, there is one striking exception: a mining town by the name of Cerro de Pasco, located in Peru. In most respects, it is much like any other little village the world over; it differs in that it is located at an altitude of 14,385 feet above sea level.

The people who visit this little town from the lower levels find themselves in a tricky, unnatural environment. They are weak and dizzy after walking a few steps, and their tortured chests heave in the attempt to get enough oxygen for their famished lungs; the slightest exertion makes them see spots before their eyes. They are also subject to fainting and dizzy spells.

On the other hand, the natives of Cerro de Pasco are not troubled by the altitude; they work and play as happily as though they were living at sea level. Examination of their bodies indicates that they differ physically from those who live at lower levels. Their lungs are larger, and they have enlarged and thickened hearts. Their veins are distended; their blood is more viscous than normal and carries larger corpuscles. Generally, their hearts beat slowly and their bodies react like those of well-trained athletes.

The animals in this high world exhibit the same physical characteristics. The horses look thin and scrawny, but they are able to outrun the lowland horses with ease at South American race tracks. These animals from a lofty climate are barred from many meetings because of their superior performance.

From our viewpoint, the most violent and venomous climate is that which is encountered on the uppermost mountains. The challenge to the human machine is incredible while climbing them; for this reason, man has ranked the conquest of the high mountain peaks among his most superb physical accomplishments.

Mount Everest in the Himalayas, called the "Goddess Mother of the World" by the natives living on the frozen steppes beneath her awesome shadow, is officially recognized as the highest mountain on the face of the earth. During World War II, one of the pilots flying the Hump drifted far north of his course and reported a peak which towered over 30,000 feet in the Anne Machin Mountains, a mysterious, unexplored range northeast of Tibet. His discovery, however, was made by radar echoes observed from a height of

28,000 feet and has never been confirmed. Despite this one possible tarnish on her reputation, Everest remains the queen of them all, remote, mysterious, and, until recently, unconquered.

Before 1852, Everest was known as Mount Chomolungma by the Tibetans and labelled simply as Peak XV by British surveyors. Legend and hearsay held that she jutted upward to wondrous heights, but no man could say how far. Then, in that year, a worker for the Indian Trigonometrical Survey was collating mountain elevations from data collected by that organization. Without leaving his office, he discovered that Everest was the loftiest protuberance on the face of this earth and calculated its height as exactly 29,002 feet. Although this figure is somewhat in doubt today, his feat still remains one of the most remarkable examples of armchair exploration on record.

Since 1921 there have been 12 expeditions launched to climb Everest, and at least 12 lives have been sacrificed in the effort. Until May 29, 1953, no man ever returned successfully from the top; on the eve of Queen Elizabeth's coronation the news was flashed around the world that a New Zealand bee-keeper, Edmund Hilary, and a Sherpa guide named Tensing Norkay had planted the British Union Jack on the summit.

The conquest of Everest's fearsome slopes presented one of the most challenging physical problems known to modern man. The top is one vast icecap, battered by terrible winds and violent storms of snow and sleet. The ridges and gorges which must be climbed are filled with treacherous ice and are subject to sudden destructive avalanches. The average wind blows at the rate of 100 miles per hour; the mean temperature is well below zero. Often winds of hurricane force strike without warning beneath a clear sky, hurling stones with the speed of cannon balls.

Many other mountains which men have conquered hold these perils. As a matter of fact, experienced mountaineers have made the statement that Everest, relatively speaking, is advantageously formed for climbing. They contend that mountains such as the Matterhorn, the sheer sides of which provide neither protection nor foothold, are much more impregnable.

Why, then, did it take so long to conquer Everest?

Some of those who tried and failed have provided a ready answer. It was not the mountain which defeated them, but the weather and the lack of oxygen. One mountaineer spoke of the terrible lassitude which overcomes a climber near the summit. Men who have worked for months with burning dedication to the task suddenly lose all ambition during the last few thousand feet. They suffer strange mental aberrations, and their reactions are dull. They speak of vague dreams and the inability to form coherent sentences as their minds vacillate between unrelated ideas. One climber remembers asking for a pick-axe, but when the word formed on his lips, he was surprised to hear himself calling for a shoe. Numbed by the constant frost, beaten by the howling winds, and weakened by the lack of oxygen, many would-be conquerors have been forced to turn back.

When men seek to live on the levels above 21,000 feet, physical deterioration sets in rapidly. Even the hardiest lose weight and there is a general wasting away of tissues and muscle. Strength and vitality decrease markedly. The lack of oxygen affects men in many different ways. Some vomit and others have blinding headaches; perhaps half of them cannot sleep at all, while others must fight to stay awake. One mountaineer found that he had to take ten breaths instead of his normal one for each step forward. There is no escape from the biting winds and relentless cold. More than any other factor, the unfamiliar, terrifying climate of the upper levels stalemated many attempts to climb the mountain.

In order to live at all in the rarefied atmosphere of Everest, a certain period of acclimatization is necessary. Colonel John Hunt, who led the successful 1953 expedition, sent his climbers high on the peak three weeks in advance so that their lungs could learn to function efficiently in the thin air. Oxygen bottles are helpful, but most mountain climbers refuse to depend entirely upon them. If the system should fail high on the barren rocks, the men would most surely be doomed were their lungs not accustomed to altitude. Gasping like netted fish, they would flounder drunkenly, unable to negotiate the easiest of slopes.

Mountaineers who have taken part in these expeditions tell strange tales of a weird race of wild men who inhabit the upper reaches of

Everest. Many footprints of these creatures, whom the Sherpas call Yetis, or Abominable Snow Men, were found above the 19,000-foot level by the 1951 expedition. Their tracks indicate that they have broad flat feet without arches. Tensing has seen one of them from a distance of 25 yards. He describes the Yeti as a creature, half man, half beast, about five and one-half feet tall, who stands upright and is able to run very fast on his heavy legs. His body is covered with reddish-brown hair, and he has a thick chest and a tall, somewhat pointed head. Efforts to follow and capture the Yetis have always been defeated by their speed and the agility with which they traverse the glaciers and cliffs of the mountain. Like much of the mountain itself, they remain a mystery. The explanation that they are a species of bear or monkey is not satisfactory to those who have seen their tracks. There is, however, one thing about which we can be certain concerning these strange inhabitants of Everest: they must be truly superbeings to withstand the hardships of the climate and atmosphere in which they live.

With the climbing of Everest, man completed a conquest that was millions of years in the making, the conquest of a planet. He has now set foot upon every major area of his globe. In a universe of cosmic forces that could smash him by a barely perceptible movement, he has demonstrated full survival ability on at least one stellar body. He has done so by stages, from nonexistence to dependence, and then to symbiotic partnership. From his local beginning, he has swarmed to cover the mountains, valleys and seas of his earth. This procedure has taken him less than 50,000 years, a cosmic instant.

What new adventures lie ahead?

During recent years scientists have probed far into the soundless void of outer space. On December 30, 1950, a glider flown by W. S. Ivans, Jr., soared without power to an altitude of over 42,000 feet, showing that strong vertical currents extend through the entire troposphere. On July 17, 1962, Major Robert M. White, United States Air Force, climbed 314,750 feet in the American X-15-1 high-speed aircraft. Rockets carrying electronic equipment have penetrated into space far beyond the outer limits of the sea of air. From these flights we have learned many unique facts about the upper regions of our atmospheric prison.

For example, scientists have found that the ozone shields us from the powerful ultraviolet radiation of the sun. Without this protection, the green earth would soon become a brown cinder.

With these high-altitude soundings as a basis, Dr. Fritz Haber has calculated that no aircraft of the designs we now use can expect to fly at altitudes much above 100,000 feet. Dr. Haber found that such a spacecraft must travel at extremely high speed in order to gain enough lift from its wings to support its weight. Although the atmosphere at this altitude is incredibly thin, the friction encountered in the necessary speed ranges would destroy the plane as effectively as the friction caused by an atmosphere of pure molasses. The pilot of such a craft would be faced with the alternative of flying fast enough to gain lift and burning himself up or of flying slower and falling down.

Indeed, the known terrors which face our new explorers rival the superstitions which beset the crews of Columbus; without doubt, there are many more obstacles still to be encountered. We can only be sure of one fact: man will attempt to surmount them.

There can be no question that we stand on the threshold of new adventures. From the vantage point of earth, man will seek to reach the stars and establish his environment and culture upon them. He will also shape his home planet and change its face to meet his needs. But whether we are inward or outward bound, our race has begun to let go of its shackles; the next step will be from passive partnership to active control of the previously unconquerable environmental forces around us.

CO_2 pellets were used by Air Force scientists to create this crater in the cloud cover.

15. The Garden Planet

It has been at least 3,000,000,000 years since the earth was hurled forth as a flaming orb to spin and cool in space. The first life-thing made room for itself in the primeval ooze more than 1,000,000,000 years ago. Fossilized remains tell us that mammals strode about the earth for 60,000,000 years. Man, by comparison, is a very recent inhabitant. His primitive ancestors have been traced back no more than 50,000 years. His recorded civilization is 7,000 years old at the most, and his science is much younger still. By far, the bulk of his achievements have been made within the last three centuries: physics is no older than 200 years; electronics and atomics are products of the last few decades.

Yet in his comparatively brief existence, man has successfully met the challenge of his environ-ment. It has been said that his forward progress is almost too successful, since the ever-growing population already crowds the fertile areas of the earth. Fifty years ago, the prospects for the race looked bleak indeed; some scientists forecast the day when the huge numbers of living humans would reduce all of us to semi-starvation. Today, however, this outlook has been drastically altered by the advance of scientific knowledge. We have begun to control the weather and extract energy from the sun. In a very literal sense, we are already mining the atmosphere, and man's ancient dream of a garden planet grows daily nearer reality.

Looking back, we can see many mistakes. For example, the first step to control of the atmosphere should have been taken in the middle of the 19th century, for it was then that Dr. David Livingstone made a remarkable discovery in the most remote part of the African jungle.

Dr. Livingstone was studying the strange practices of the natives and had become friendly with Sechale, one of Africa's greatest witch doctors. One summer day he was approached by the tribe's medicine man and told that Sechale was about to make rain. Was the Doctor interested? He certainly was.

Sechale explained that the drought cure was charcoal of a special magical kind. The recipe called for burning a pungent mixture of bat wings, jackal livers, excretions from a mountain pony, serpent skins, the hearts of baboons, lion hair, and various tubers, bulbs, and roots found in the African bush country. After the charcoal was made, it was burned on the windward side of the clouds so that its magic incense penetrated them from below. Livingstone scoffed and told the medicine man that the clouds were not charmed by his odorous smoke. He was amazed at the amount of rain which resulted from the experiment. The good doctor jotted down the formula and included it in one of his books. Thus, without realizing it, Dr. Livingstone wrote the first practical textbook on weather control.

One hundred years later, in 1953, United States scientists of the Water Resources Development Corporation placed 12 waist-high pots in the desert near Lake Dallas, Texas. These did not contain bats or baboons, but the principle was precisely the same. A pungent chemical mixture of silver iodide was allowed to heat, releasing a billowy smoke which drifted up against the windward side of the clouds overhead. This smoke was created for 870 hours over a six-month period. A check of the water storage showed that the level in the Dallas drainage basin had increased over 350%. Other reservoirs nearby had fallen or had barely held their own during the same period.

With all his chanting of secret words and magic dances, Sechale had stumbled upon a scientific and extremely useful discovery. But it took a very long time for weathermen to grasp the idea, even though they had been confronted with it for many years. The Indians of the central plains had dotted their reservations with rain fires to coax the sulky rain god while they beat their tom-toms. Still, no forecaster ever made a pre-diction of rain based on their activities. These were considered just another wild native superstition.

It remained for two European scientists, Walter Findersen and Tor Bergeron, to realize that the Indians and African savages might have something. Shortly after World War I, Bergeron explained that the vast bulk of moisture in the air existed as droplets so small that they are invisible to the human eye. The vertical movement within the great weather fronts, said Bergeron, caused this moisture to condense into clouds by the process of cooling. He visualized this action as being similar to that which occurs on the windshields of our cars when they become foggy on cold winter mornings. As the vertical movement continues, some of the water particles are carried into still cooler regions and another amazing phenomenon takes place. Instead of freezing at 32°, the normal freezing point of water, the droplets maintain their liquid form all the way to −39°. Water in this state is called supercooled; its formation baffles scientists to this day.

Bergeron postulated that when the air-borne water droplets reached a given critical size, they fell as rain. The trick in rainmaking, then, was to find some artificial means of increasing the droplet size in the potential rain clouds.

The two scientists quickly discovered that dust particles and other floating matter in the atmosphere act as condensation nuclei, collecting water droplets into still larger droplets, which soon become heavy enough to fall as rain. Ice crystals formed by the freezing of supercooled water droplets were observed to be very efficient drop-collectors. Perhaps the idea seemed too fantastic to practical men, for the scientists were not able to obtain financial support for their experiments and nothing further was done until 1946.

In that year, the scientists of the General Electric plant in Schenectady, New York, revived the experiments by simulating the conditions of the atmosphere in the laboratory. Drs. Irving Langmuir, Vincent Schaefer, and Bernard Vonnegut conducted basic research on the subject, which culminated in the joint United States Army, Navy and Air Force effort called Project Cirrus.

Some of these early experiments on super-

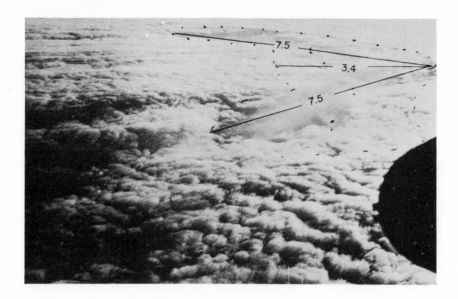

Clouds seeded during Project Cirrus give up their moisture and fade away. Perhaps these techniques will some day enable us to control our weather.

cooled clouds were fascinating in their simplicity. In the course of their studies, the General Electric scientists delved into some very basic cloud physics. One of the things they could not explain was the high percentage of water clouds encountered at temperatures below freezing. If water freezes at 32°, why is it that clouds do not turn into ice crystals when they fall to this temperature?

Dr. Schaefer produced some water droplets with temperatures below freezing in an ordinary home-freezer unit by blowing his breath into the cooler. The clouds formed at zero degrees but very few ice crystals were observed in the clouds themselves. Various substances, such as silica, carbon, graphite, and many others, were tried without success as nuclei to initiate ice-crystal formation.

One torrid July day the cold box was sluggish in its cooling-down process. To speed up the cooling, a piece of dry ice was placed in the box. In an instant the cloud became a mass of glittering ice crystals. Dr. Schaefer blew his breath into the cloud of ice crystals, but now, instead of becoming a water cloud, the cloud soon disappeared and condensed on the ice crystals.

What caused this dramatic change from liquid to solid? Subsequent work showed that water has a critical temperature of −39°. Below this temperature it will always turn to ice, even without the presence of dust or other foreign particles. Anything that will reduce the temperature of the water below this figure will cause ice-crystal formation.

Some rapid calculations showed that a piece of dry ice about the size of a pea can produce enough ice crystals to seed a cubic mile of clouds. With this thought in mind, Dr. Schaefer hired a private plane on the morning of November 13, 1946. The previous evening he had studied weather maps and temperature soundings and had found that a good possibility of supercooled clouds existed on the following day. The morning of the flight he made a final check on the weather and found a promising situation in the local area. His associates helped break up some dry ice into fine particles, and he and his pilot climbed into the plane. They took off and headed for the Mount Greylock area, while Dr. Langmuir observed from the ground. As they approached the potential seeding point some isolated patches of altostratus clouds, several thousand feet thick, were observed, and they climbed over the top of these clouds. After making preliminary observations to see if the clouds were composed of supercooled water droplets or ice crystals, they decided that the clouds were water-laden and began to sprinkle dry ice into them. After a few passes over the cloud deck, they flew off to one side to observe the results of the seeding.

Trailing wisps of snow were falling out of the base of the seeded clouds. The unmistakable signs of successful cloud-seeding were visible even to Langmuir at Schenectady some 40 miles away. A quick glance at the nearby patches of unseeded clouds revealed no snow or rain falling.

History was being made. Man now could directly alter nature's plans. The sense of awe ex-

124

perienced by the General Electric scientists must have rivalled that felt by the nuclear scientists witnessing the explosion of the first A-bomb at Alamogordo, New Mexico.

Further advances were rapidly made. Dr. Vonnegut discovered that water droplets could not distinguish between true ice and silver-iodide crystals. Experimentation proved that silver iodide, burned from ground dispensers, sometimes produced rain even more efficiently than dry ice and at a much lower cost. Two pennies' worth of silver iodide is enough to seed up to five hundred cubic miles of supercooled clouds.

The experiments by Langmuir and Schaefer opened up a whole new branch of meteorology. Man was now in a position to do something about the weather besides just talking about it.

Many authorities read a deep significance into man's ability to unlock the treasure of air-borne moisture. They predict that the vast arid areas throughout the world may be transformed into food bowls to feed the growing population of earth. Storm control appears possible within the next 40 years. The deadly hurricanes, tornadoes, and thunderstorms are all erected upon a foundation of supercooled clouds. We may be able to alter the structure of these storms by seeding them, so that they collapse before they become damaging.

Perhaps the greatest benefit we can hope to gain is an economic one. The welfare of many nations rests on the narrow margin between plentiful food supply and famine produced by a dry year. The great blight of our world, hunger, may be reduced by the successful application of weather-modification projects. A practical rain-making scheme which would ensure ample irrigation in India and the Near Eastern countries might win far more friends for the West than any amount of aid scattered over the dry rice paddies.

The 17,000,000,000,000 tons of water in the air offer a bountiful harvest if we can successfully reap it. But the atmosphere contains even greater riches. More than 1,000,000,000,000,000 kilowatt hours of energy beat unceasingly upon the earth's surface each day, radiated by the sun. This daily flow of energy is comparable to all the known reserves of coal, oil, falling water, natural gas, thorium, and uranium on the earth.

The possibility of harnessing this vast solar energy has been the hope of scientists ever since it became apparent that the fuel supplies of earth were approaching exhaustion. Although a search for fuel is always on, newly discovered sources of power fail to replace the depletion of existing reserves by our growing industrial civilization. Even atomic energy offers little relief from this dilemma. The costliness of nuclear material for general usage, coupled with its limited supply, indicates only temporary relief.

As a consequence, man has turned to the great quantity of energy which pours upon him from outer space; the scientists who are searching to tap the sun's rays have followed many trails. Efforts have been made to trap the sunlight by enormous mirrors. These have been focussed upon water to split its molecules into basic hydrogen and oxygen, which could then be burned as fuel. This process has been partially successful, but not more than one part in 100 of the solar energy has been harnessed by means of it.

During 1954 a development occurred which may become the most revolutionary of our age. This was the construction of the first solar battery. Compounded out of commonplace materials with no moving parts, it is a device which theoretically should last forever. Very possibly, with further development, it will open the door to the unlimited energy of the sun.

The solar battery was developed by a scientific task team of the Bell Telephone Laboratories in New York. The heart of this device is composed of very thin strips of silicon, the most common substance to be found on the surface of our earth. Each of these strips is about the thickness of a razor blade, and for some mysterious reason an electric current flows within them when they are exposed to sunlight. If they are linked together, they will provide power from the sun at the rate of 50 watts per square yard of exposed surface. The power generated represents 6% of the total sun power falling on the battery. This is comparable to the energy our steam engines and oil-powered motors extract from their fuels, with no engines to stroke and no dams to build.

Ultimately, the applications for the solar battery as a power source are limitless. Incorporation of the silicon sheets in the roofs of private homes may supply all the requirements of lighting, electrical power, and heating for the lifetime of the house and for no additional expense. Conceivably, this revolutionary development may make electrical energy among the world's cheapest and most plentiful commodities.

During these years when man has been conquering his environment of gases, he has also been changing its form and texture. Serious concern has been expressed recently over the long-range effects of some of this pollution. The prime source of worry has been the recent experiments with atomic and hydrogen bombs; we have become familiar with such phrases as the "fallout effect" and "mutations due to radioactivity." There are many who say that exploding the big bombs is like pouring deadly arsenic into a pond: the fish will surely die.

Prince Louis de Broglie, a leading French physicist and Nobel Prize winner, believes that the danger mark has already been reached for the world's plant and animal life. He lists several causes for his concern.

According to de Broglie, there is a possibility that the vast amount of nitric acid created by H-bomb explosions may upset the chemical balance of the atmosphere and scorch the earth's vegetation. The millions of tons of debris thrown high into the upper atmosphere may form condensation nuclei to act as a gigantic, uncontrollable, rain-making project which produces far-reaching effects on the pattern of the winds. Also, this air-borne garbage may ultimately shroud part of the globe in semi-gloom, creating a new ice age of swift and terrible expansion to descend upon us. Not the least of his misgivings is associated with the long-term effects of releasing gamma radiation into the air. There are sound reasons for believing that even a small increase in the radiation content of the atmosphere will produce drastic changes for the future inhabitants of our globe.

De Broglie's concern is echoed by other groups. The increase in air-borne radioactivity is already a serious nuisance to scientists who date ancient objects by means of radioactive carbon 14. This substance has a radiation lifetime of many thousands of years, and by analyzing fossils for carbon 14 it is possible accurately to date their origin. However, laboratories near the Nevada atom-bomb test site can no longer use this method. There is too much general radioactivity in the area.

Similar experiences have been encountered on the eastern seaboard of the United States when radioactive clouds drift in overhead. So far, the activity has not been strong enough to injure health, but the delicate measuring apparatus in many laboratories gives false readings. If the big bombs are exploded in greater numbers, one of the results may be that scientists will have to abandon an outstanding method for dating ancient objects. However, this disadvantage will probably go unnoticed because of other results far more devastating.

Non-atomic pollution of the atmosphere is also a current hazard. Increasing world population and industrial expansion are releasing all sorts of pollution into the air. A great deal of this is in the form of carbon dioxide, and some scientists attribute the general warming of the earth's climate to this cause. Temperature records kept

A racetrack pattern flown by a Project Cirrus aircraft.

during the past 100 years indicate a rise of two degrees. The great glaciers have been retreating along the northern rim of the world, and the cold-water fish are migrating northward. Industrial smog grows worse each year. It is estimated that the London smog carries with it more than 5,000,000 tons of sulphur dioxide alone. To this must be added the soot, the ashes, and the other wastes which coat our buildings and lungs.

The prophets who predict the doom of the human race see much import in all of this. To be sure, there are many menacing elements in our universe for those who are inclined to be afraid. But we who face the possible dangers of the H-bomb fallout are of the same species as those who discovered the timeless laws of electricity and mechanics. If we stand today in the face of destruction, we also stand at the threshold of space travel. This too will be of our own making.

For most of his brief span, man has not understood that he lives within a sea of gases resembling in many ways the sea of water which encompasses the land. Indeed, during the infant days of his existence, he held many strange superstitions about the atmosphere which are incredible to his enlightened brethren of today.

But the real miracle is not that man was once without knowledge, but that he has managed to learn at all. It was truly remarkable when Copernicus decided that the world was round, for the globe reaches outward, flat and level, as far as the eye can see; its curvature could not be felt or known by any faculty other than the human brain. The discovery that the air has substance, just as the rocks or the mountains and the water of the rivers, was equally wondrous, because air, like the faith in man's heart, has neither shape nor color. Its structure has the texture of a dream and its form is no more definite than flowing sand.

The great tower of discovery reaches endlessly up, and many hands work to build it higher still. The achievements we have already recorded and the enterprise within us now make it plain that vast new ages full of promise lie before our race. And we will climb to meet them, even though the stairs are dark and we have no light to guide us, except that of our own courageous, questing spirit.